Introductio

I am a married mother of 3 children, living in Leicester and working as a speech and language teacher in schools. I decided to write this book because when my eldest daughter, Anna, was diagnosed with idiopathic scoliosis (curved spine) at the age of 14, I hadn't even heard of the condition. I immediately wanted to find out what scoliosis actually is, what tests Anna could expect, whether surgery would be necessary, if so what it would entail, and so on.

I have no specific writing experience but write from a mother's perspective and in language suitable, I believe, for communicating to all the parents in the world who are still reeling from the shock of their child receiving the diagnosis of scoliosis like a bolt out of the blue.

This book details Anna's diagnosis, treatment and subsequent recovery, and tells how the diagnosis impacted not only on Anna but the whole family over a two-year period from diagnosis to one year post-surgery.

In the UK, scoliosis affects three to four children out of every 100 and can develop at any time during childhood and adolescence (the teenage years). It is more common in girls than boys and often occurs at the start of their adolescence.

In about 8 out of 10 cases of scoliosis, the cause is unknown. This is medically known as idiopathic scoliosis. However, researchers have found that in about a third of idiopathic scoliosis cases, the child has some family history of the condition, which suggests a genetic link.

Scoliosis is not caused by bad posture, exercise, diet, or wearing heavy rucksacks.

Scoliosis that is present at birth is known as congenital scoliosis. This is rare and is caused by the bones in the spine developing abnormally in the womb.

In most cases the onset of the scoliosis is gradual and usually painless. Sometimes a mild to moderate scoliosis can develop without being noticed by the child or his / her parents. This is often because the condition usually develops at the age when children tend to become more self-conscious (age 9 to 14) and don't often have their back exposed.

However, the more severe the scoliosis, the more disfiguring it can become. This is because when the spine curves sideways, as the curve becomes more severe the small bones that make up the spine (the vertebrae) also twist round. This pulls any attached muscles, ligaments and ribs round with them. As a consequence, if the scoliosis is in the chest (thoracic) region, the ribs and shoulder blade stick out like a bulge on one side of the back. The more severe the scoliosis, the larger the bulge. Also one shoulder may hang lower than the other, and one shoulder blade may be higher than the other.

If the scoliosis is in the lumbar (lower back) region it can make the pelvis thrust forward on one side and one leg may appear to be shorter than the other.

If scoliosis becomes severe and is not treated, it can cause problems later in life.

In some cases of scoliosis the diagnosis is obvious. However, some mild cases are not so obvious. A quick test, which a doctor or nurse may do, is simply to ask the child to bend forward. A bulge on the back of the chest is more obvious when bending forward. If a doctor or nurse diagnoses scoliosis you will normally be referred to a specialist.

X-ray pictures can show the spine clearly. From the pictures a specialist can assess the angle of the curve. This gives an idea of the severity of the condition and the likelihood of it getting worse.

Treatment depends on various factors such as the patient's age, whether they are still growing, the severity of the curve, the exact location of the scoliosis (for example, upper or lower back) and the chance that it may progress. Treatment options include observation, bracing and surgery.

Most cases are mild and do not need any treatment, as they stay the same or get better in time. Others, however, get worse as the child grows. Therefore, even for mild cases a specialist is likely to arrange regular reviews to make sure that the condition does not get much worse.

For children diagnosed around puberty or early teens, the reviews may be every 3-6 months or so. Once the main bone growth ends after puberty, scoliosis does not usually become worse. In most cases there is usually no restriction on sports or other activities. In some cases a specialist may advise against certain activities such as to avoid heavy contact sports or gymnastics.

For children diagnosed as babies, the review may be more frequent. In many cases diagnosed in babies, the condition gets better on its own as the child grows. However, some cases become worse rather quickly and treatment may be needed to prevent it becoming severe.

If the scoliosis is moderate or progressing, then a back brace may be advised. A brace does not cure a scoliosis. The aim of a brace is to prevent the scoliosis from getting worse as the child grows, so it is more commonly used when scoliosis is diagnosed before or early on in the growth spurt of puberty. If used, a brace is worn most of the day and night. A child can do most normal activities while wearing a back brace. However, the use of these braces is controversial and your specialist will advise on the pros and cons.

An operation on the spine is the only way to permanently correct a scoliosis. It is a long and major operation and usually only considered for severe cases. However, the long-term results of the operation are usually good.

Very few children (about 1 in 350) will require surgery to correct the position of their spine: Anna was one of these children.

Help – My Daughter Has Scoliosis

How Anna overcame her curve
and followed her dream

Help – My Daughter Has Scoliosis

How Anna overcame her curve
and followed her dream

Hilary Lowne

ISBN: 978-0-9573400-0-8

Published by Hilary Lowne in conjunction with Writersworld, this book is produced entirely in the UK, is available to order from most book shops in the United Kingdom, and is also globally available via UK-based Internet book retailers.

Copy edited by Sue Croft

Cover design by Jag Lall

www.writersworld.co.uk

WRITERSWORLD
2 Bear Close Flats
Bear Close
Woodstock
Oxfordshire
OX20 1JX
United Kingdom

The text pages of this book are produced via an independent certification process that ensures the trees from which the paper is produced come from well managed sources that exclude the risk of using illegally logged timber while leaving options to use post-consumer recycled paper as well.

Acknowledgements

I would like to thank the following people who have made this book possible.

Firstly to Graham Cook and his fantastic team, Sue Croft and Jag Lall, for their expertise, support and professionalism throughout the whole publishing process.

To all of the superb doctors, nurses and physiotherapists at the Queen's Medical Centre, Nottingham, for all of their skill and care in not only performing the operation but also for giving such wonderful aftercare and support.

To the medical staff at the Leicester Royal Infirmary and the Croft Medical Centre who looked after Anna so well.

To Theresa, our fantastic physiotherapist, for helping Anna in so many ways.

To all my work colleagues at Braunstone Frith Infants School who were so supportive throughout.

To my good friend Sheila, in reading chapters and providing positive feedback!

To all my family and friends who offered support, advice, texts, comfort and helped us all keep a sense of humour and feeling of positivity throughout.

To my wonderful husband, Andrew, who had faith in my abilities to write and, together with Matthew and Rachel, provided laughter and fun when Anna and I needed it in the early post-op days.

And finally, to Anna, whose resilience and outlook on life has made me so proud.

Dedication

For Anna

and Andrew, Matthew and Rachel

Contents

ONE

A shocking discovery

I was just hauling a basket of washing outside one glorious Saturday afternoon in May 2010 when I heard my eldest daughter, Anna, calling down to me from upstairs.

"Mum!"

I pretended, as I occasionally did, not to have heard, and blithely carried on pegging.

"Mum! Quickly!" Another shout, this time louder and more insistent followed, so feeling slightly irritated that Anna couldn't be bothered to come downstairs and talk properly, I went to find out what the problem was.

She was in our double bedroom, standing in front of the mirrored wardrobe, twisting herself round in an attempt to see her back.

Anna was fourteen and had been clothes shopping with friends in town earlier that day, and on returning home had disappeared upstairs, keen to try out the new strappy tops bought in preparation for the summer ahead.

"What is it?" My question sounded quite abrupt because I couldn't see what the urgency was.

"My hips are wonky. Look!" Anna looked at me quizzically, waiting for my response.

"What do you mean?" I smiled. "Your hips are meant to be curvy."

But as I talked, very calmly at that point, I could see

clearly that one of her hips did seem to jut out sideways, much more than the other side, which made her look as though she wasn't standing up straight.

Before I could really think about what to say next, she added casually, " —and my back doesn't look straight. What do you think? . . . Is my back straight?"

I held her shoulders, gently turned her round and immediately felt a tremendous surge of panic and disbelief as I saw her spine. Her slender build made it very easy for me to see that the top of her spine was perfectly straight, but a couple of inches further down noticeably curved out towards the right before coming back to the centre further down her back.

I was totally shocked. Horrified. I had not expected to see this and didn't know what to say.

"Anna! Your back is twisted! It's not straight." My thoughts tumbled out unchecked and the panic, disbelief and fear in my words echoed the look on Anna's face.

For a few uncertain seconds we both stared at each other; but the shocked silence was soon broken.

"What's happened? What's wrong with my back?" Anna was panicking now and twisting round to get a better view for herself.

That was the same question bouncing around my head and it was quickly followed by other questions rushing forwards and filling me with fear. *What is wrong with her back? When did this happen? How could I have missed it? What are we going to do? What caused it? Could I have prevented it?*

My mind was whirling with the enormity of what I was seeing, but I knew my initial unthinking response, agreeing that her back wasn't straight, had scared her.

I tried to alleviate her panic with reassurances.

"Don't worry, it's really not that bad. I've probably over-reacted. I'm sorry. Your spine doesn't seem completely straight but perhaps it will straighten as you grow and I'm sure our GP will know what to do." I couldn't think of any other advice to give and felt quite inadequate on how to deal with the situation.

As her mum I was used to making sure life ran smoothly and resolving any problem she thrust at me, but at that moment I felt helpless and very worried that something could be seriously wrong. I had never seen a curved spine before and had not expected this situation at all; there was no preparation or gentle realisation that had built up over time. Just this shocking discovery on a previously normal day. After all, Anna was a healthy girl and hadn't had any health issues or weaknesses. It just didn't seem right.

I suddenly felt, in that moment, that something in our lives had changed. Some tiny voice inside my head was firing alarm bells that filled me with anxiety and apprehension. Thankfully, my bland reassurances seemed to calm Anna and I began to admire all her new clothes and share her excitement about our summer holiday, but inwardly my heart was pounding and I didn't know what to think. Anna was so sporty and active and had hardly ever had a day off school. This couldn't be happening to her.

I was surprised that Anna didn't continue to question me about it, and worry, because my explanations seemed rather feeble even to me, but she matter-of-factly appeared to have accepted my suggestions and started talking about our forthcoming holiday in Malta that July and how much fun it would be.

As she bent forwards to collect the strewn clothes off the bed, I kept my eyes fixed on her back. Her new cream top, decorated in intricate navy flowers with delicate straps looked so elegant, but all I can remember thinking was relief that she liked such thin, dainty straps or she may not have even noticed this curve. I couldn't believe that *I* hadn't noticed it.

I felt very negligent. Surely I should have somehow noticed what had happened to her back. Now we had spotted it, it seemed so obvious, and I felt angry with myself for not realising that her spine had changed so radically.

When my husband, Andrew, arrived home a few hours later I bombarded him with the worrying news and all the questions that were still unanswered. However, he didn't seem overly concerned about Anna's back at that point and thought that our GP would have all the answers we needed, and even speculated that it could be a fairly common condition, despite the fact we'd never seen anything like it ourselves.

With hindsight it was probably a good thing that we were ignorant of the facts at that stage because we didn't cause Anna any worry as the weekend continued. Andy is a very relaxed person and tends not to get unduly anxious about the children, leaving all the worrying to me!

And, of course, I was very concerned indeed, and I wanted more information immediately to satisfy my desire for answers. Naturally, what I really wanted to hear was that it was a common problem found in many teenagers and would resolve by itself. I determinedly opened my laptop that evening and focused on searching for answers.

There was a wealth of information waiting for me on the internet, mostly medical sites and articles, which included many photographs and diagrams, and by the end of the evening I guess I already knew the answer to my biggest question: whether or not Anna had scoliosis.

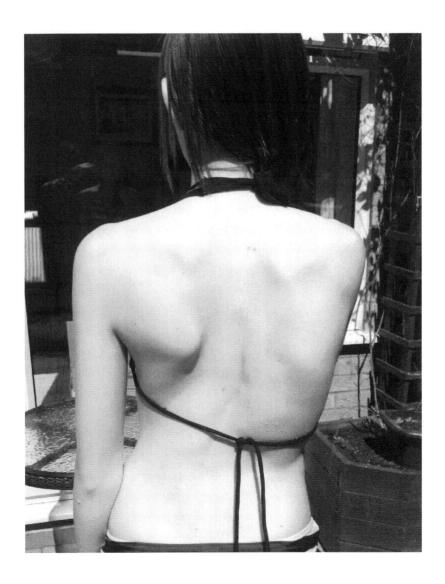

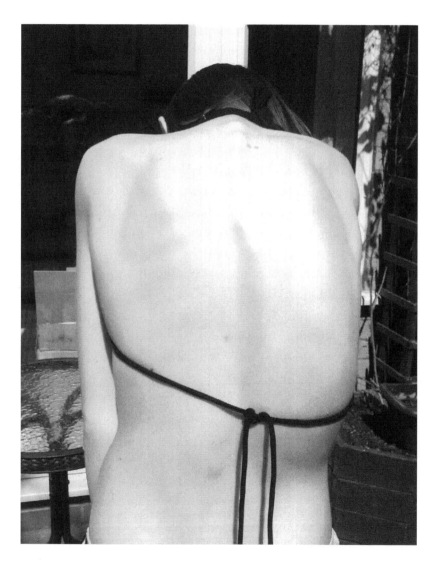

The first time we saw Anna's curve

TWO

Scoliosis confirmed

We needed to see a doctor as soon as possible, so it was at 7:50 the following Monday morning that Anna and I waited in the steadily forming queue outside our doctor's surgery; morning appointments were given on a first come, first served basis, and we wanted an appointment before school started.

Anna was in her final year at middle school and hoped to transfer to Beauchamp College in Leicester that September to start studying for her GCSEs. There is never a good time to have a medical condition and I really hoped any diagnosis wouldn't impact on her schoolwork, or in fact any aspect of her life.

At 8:10am the red flashing sign informed us that our GP could see us. Everything was running smoothly so far. Once we had sat down, Anna calmly explained what we had seen in the bedroom and how her hips seemed out of line, hoping that it was probably a common occurrence in teenagers.

However, following a brief examination of her back, our GP kindly explained to Anna that she did indeed have scoliosis. A referral to a paediatric orthopaedic consultant was now necessary and as soon as possible. This was a big shock to me, even though I had suspected such a diagnosis, and I sat back with disbelief etched on my mind. Our doctor then told us that she would type the referral letter and ensure it was sent that day. We could then expect an appointment within six weeks.

Anna received the news calmly (while I was sitting outwardly calm but inwardly in turmoil and extremely anxious about what would happen next, having really hoped that we had been mistaken) and asked about the long-term prognosis.

Unfortunately, the doctor couldn't give any specific reassurances because we needed an x-ray to evaluate how curved her spine was, so she advised her to write down all the questions she had, to ask at the hospital appointment. Anna told me afterwards that she had many questions to write down for the consultant, but the main one in the forefront of her mind was: can I still be a dancer in the West End?

Anna had always loved dancing and as a very young girl would practise routines to favourite pop songs in her room and give 'shows' for us. She loved ballet, tap and modern, but particularly modern, and had long harboured a dream of being on the stage and in musical theatre. She had only joined her dance school as an 11 year old, but from the start loved performing in shows, and after seeing several West End musicals had decided that this was the career path for her.

As her mum, I thought that she had plenty of natural rhythm and poise plus the perfect slender build of a dancer. She was also a talented runner and enjoyed cross-country running; she had even participated at county level. This made her diagnosis seem all the more unfair because Anna was such an active person and needed the flexibility in her back for all her activities. Her competitive spirit and endeavour to win always shone through when she took dance exams or competed in races, and I knew that she would need all the determination she had to get her through the potentially difficult times ahead.

It seemed so unjust that Anna needed a strong body for dancing but now had a curved spine, and we didn't know at this stage whether or not it could be corrected and how much her flexibility and overall movement might be affected.

She was born on March 19th 1996 weighing just under 8lbs and very healthy. It was only eight hours after her birth that I was allowed home, delighted to be bringing with me a healthy baby girl, with no indication that a condition was waiting to reveal itself once she hit puberty.

Anna is our second child. Matt had been born 19 months earlier in July 1994 and Rachel, her younger sister, in December 2001. We are a very ordinary family living in Leicester in the East Midlands. My husband, Andrew, had started his own flooring business three years earlier and I worked as a part-time speech and language therapist. None of the children had had any health problems apart from a broken arm and elbow (Rachel) and a torn tendon following a bike accident (Matt). In fact, Anna was the one who had never been in hospital for anything and had only had one course of antibiotics for an infected wart in her entire life. She hadn't even had a dental filling.

We finally left the surgery that May morning feeling relieved that we were now 'in the system' and that Anna could be helped. We didn't really know at this stage what sort of help that would be and what choices lay ahead.

I dropped Anna off at school in plenty of time for her first lesson and we all carried on with the day, pushing the diagnosis well and truly to the backs of our minds. All we could do now was wait for the hospital appointment, which unfortunately was a process that could not be hurried. We just had to wait for our turn.

That anxiously awaited turn finally came exactly six weeks after our visit to the doctor, when our appointment arrived in the post, scheduled for a Monday afternoon in July at the paediatric orthopaedic outpatient clinic at the Leicester Royal Infirmary. We started to count down the days.

THREE

Seeing the curve

The next few weeks passed fairly quickly and uneventfully without any of us really dwelling on Anna's curve, and on July 5th I collected Anna early from school in time for the 2 o'clock appointment.

I'm the sort of person who has to be early for an appointment or bang on time, never late (often a bone of contention between myself and Andrew who hasn't the same anxiety!), so I had allowed plenty of time to park and find the outpatient clinic.

We both sat calmly in the waiting area because, although we were anxious about the diagnosis, we wanted some sort of treatment to begin so that Anna could go back to living normally without scoliosis hanging over her.

The room was noisy with lots of young children playing around us, who thankfully distracted us from dwelling on what would happen in the consultation.

Soon we found ourselves discussing Anna's situation with the consultant, who seemed very at ease and was quite matter-of-fact when examining Anna's spine and checking various reflexes, which were fortunately all normal. Of course, he sees many patients every year and didn't feel the anxiety that we were feeling at that point. The flexibility of her straight leg raise was normal at 90 degrees. He then confirmed that she did indeed have a right thoracic scoliosis with a prominence of ribs on the right side, but would need an x-ray to confirm the extent of the curve.

So far we had had no surprises and no new information, but an x-ray would really decide the next step. Consequently, our next wait was in the x-ray department which we both attended with some trepidation; soon we would know how curved her spine really was. This waiting room was much smaller and quieter and luckily Anna could be seen almost immediately, which was a relief to us both.

It was only thirty minutes later that we stared at the consultant's computer screen, back in the outpatient clinic, expectantly waiting for the results.

Suddenly Anna's spine flashed on the screen and that was the defining moment when I knew that everything really wasn't ok. I was visibly shocked. Seeing her bones on the black and white film highlighted the curvature starkly and made it quite clear that her spine curved 45 degrees to the right. I had never seen a curved spine and it looked so abnormal I could hardly take my eyes off the screen. Anna looked equally shocked.

The angle of curvature is called the Cobb angle measurement and provides a baseline in order to monitor any progressive increase in the size of the curvature over time.

I think up until that point I had been secretly hoping that we had over-dramatised everything and Anna wouldn't really have much of a problem because she was inherently so fit and healthy. But this x-ray blew away any hopeful thoughts in an instant.

Most people take it for granted that their back is straight and no-one really gives any thought to it, so when I saw Anna's bones growing incorrectly, particularly her spine, which is so fundamental to movement and posture, I felt a cold dread that this was definitely a real problem and I wondered how on earth it could be corrected. I just wanted Anna to be 'normal', whatever that is, and being faced with the exceptionally abnormal x-rays was very frightening. I felt totally helpless at that moment and there was nothing reassuring I could think of to say to Anna who was sitting silently besides me.

We both asked what the next course of action would be and I was surprised to hear that the consultant didn't feel that 45 degrees was particularly significant; in fact he didn't seem overly concerned at all and said it was up to us what the next step would be. He said that many people in fact walk around and live with a slightly curved spine and that 45 degrees was on the boundary of being a problem.

There were essentially two possible choices facing us; we could wait and have a further x-ray in a few months' time or we could go on the waiting list for surgery. Naturally I asked what decision our consultant felt we should make and was quite surprised when he said it was completely up to us. Because surgery is such an invasive choice with possible negative side effects, we had to be absolutely sure that this was the route we wanted to take. It did seem as though he was trying to put us off surgery, detailing all the risks and stressing what a complex and major procedure this would be, and that ultimately it was our choice.

It was hard to suddenly have to make a decision without really knowing what to do for the best, and I really wished that Andrew had been there as well to help us decide. We just didn't know what to say and I wished at that point I knew more about the condition.

After listening to all the information available to us at that point, Anna and I thought that 45 degrees was possibly not enough curvature to consider such invasive surgery at this point, and there was nothing to suggest then that Anna's back was going to get worse very quickly; every person is so different and it's difficult to predict how a curvature will progress, if at all.

The consultant agreed with our decision to wait until a further x-ray a few months down the line to see if there was any change. In the meantime we were advised to look at the British Scoliosis Society website and the Scoliosis Association UK website and then come back in four months for another x-ray and a further discussion. Our consultant also felt it would be beneficial to have an MRI scan to rule out any other factors such as spinal dysraphism.

Spinal dysraphism is a congenital defect of the neural tube, the structure that precedes the development of the spinal cord in foetuses. In normal development, the neural tube folds together precisely to form the spinal column and secure the spinal cord. Problems can arise if the neural tube never closes fully or seals together incorrectly. Symptoms in infants and growing children can range from very mild and almost unnoticeable to debilitating and disfiguring. Depending on the severity of symptoms, a treatment plan involving medication, surgery, and physiotherapy is needed to promote proper growth and development (see References, page 128 for website address for spinal dysraphism).

I sincerely hoped she did not have this condition.

The consultant also wanted to check the structural integrity of the spine, particularly as Anna had been getting frequent back pain (almost daily), although he wasn't unduly concerned about any pain and even told us that children with scoliosis 'don't get pain'! We both knew that that was a myth; when you live with someone who has never taken tablets for anything and who suddenly needed almost daily pain relief, you look for a cause. The only cause for Anna was her scoliosis.

She explained her love of running and dancing and how she couldn't do high kicks in dance any more, or run fast, because it hurt her back, and how she quickly got very out-of-breath, which had never been an issue the previous year. However, the consultant said he was happy for her to carry on with all her activities; he didn't feel that the scoliosis was a particular factor and that surgery would be more for cosmetic reasons than anything else.

We agreed with him that surgery did seem a drastic step if it might not be needed, so we were happy with our decision to wait until November and then discuss our options depending on whether there were any changes in the curve. It was a difficult decision to make and would have been much easier if we knew what the future held. The benefit of hindsight is, of course, a wonderful thing that we didn't have access to.

The appointment for the MRI scan, to check for any other abnormalities, came through very quickly and it was only two weeks later that we were in yet another waiting area, much less crowded and with quiet air of anticipation about it. After completing a short questionnaire we were ready for Anna to go in. Or so I thought!

Prior to arriving we had been told that Anna couldn't wear any metal because of the strong magnets used in the scanner (she had fixed braces on but obviously these had to stay in place and weren't going to be a problem). I presumed that she hadn't got any other metal on her but hadn't realised that there are iron filings in mascara and certainly hadn't bargained on Anna wearing make-up for an 8am scan!

Paper towels had to be substitute make-up wipes, although they were fairly ineffective as Anna found after ten minutes of scraping! However, enough was removed and she was finally ready to go in for the scan.

An MRI scan is a Magnetic Resonance Imaging scan. It uses strong magnetic fields and radio waves to take very detailed pictures of the brain or spine, or any other parts of the body.

Patients are asked to lie on a scanner table and Anna was told to mention if she felt uncomfortable because it was important that she was able to keep very still during the scan. When she was comfortable and ready she would be moved into the scanner tunnel, but staff would continue to talk to her using an intercom.

Although the MRI scan is painless, the scanner is very noisy. Each set of pictures takes about five minutes and several sets might be taken during one session, so the whole procedure usually takes about 45 minutes.

Anna had been told that she could listen to music through headphones during the scan to help pass the time. Although there was a large selection of CDs in the waiting area you could also take your own, which was Anna's original plan, but on the day she completely forgot! The music also helped drown out the noise of the machine and distract from the bumpy vibrations as the scanner did its work.

She was encouraged to close her eyes throughout as the

machine is only centimetres away from the face and body at any one time and can feel extremely claustrophobic. She later told me she had an alarm button to hold as well in case she panicked and needed to be pulled out. However, she didn't use this and only once felt close to doing so when she mistakenly opened her eyes, thinking that the scan had finished, but saw the machine so frighteningly close she immediately shut them again and focused on the music.

It actually wasn't as bad as Anna had expected and it was a relief to get it out of the way before our holiday. The whole process was over relatively quickly.

By 9.30am we were home and ready for the summer holidays to begin. We put Anna's scoliosis out of our thoughts and prepared to fly off to Malta the following day.

We had never been to this beautiful island before and stayed in a wonderful villa with its own pool and expansive terrace. The weather was absolutely glorious and meant that bikinis, strappy tops and shorts were the daily attire. Of course seeing Anna in her bikini every day made me think of her back and wonder constantly how we had failed to notice any changes in her spine over the previous year when she had been at middle school, and when an earlier diagnosis would have meant we could have monitored the situation before it got so severe. I vowed to watch Rachel's back, who was still only nine, very closely.

As it was, Anna was about to embark on her two-year GSCE course when she started at Beauchamp College in September. I wasn't sure how much this would affect her, although one change had already been made since the diagnosis, in terms of which subjects she should do. Anna had dropped the option of PE, despite loving all sport and being good at it, and taken Media Studies instead. She knew that her activity levels were already compromised and could get worse and she didn't want to start a subject only to have to transfer to a different one, part way through the year.

Since the diagnosis we had discovered two other girls living close to us who also had had scoliosis diagnosed when fourteen and fifteen years respectively and whose parents also didn't notice any changes until the curve was very obvious. They too couldn't believe they hadn't noticed any curvature when their daughters were younger and this was reassuring because I had felt so negligent that I hadn't seen the curve earlier.

One of these girls, Ruth, had had the operation several years earlier and had later gone on to run the London Marathon, which helped us feel that Anna's dream of dancing could still be realised.

The other girl, Emma, was a friend of Matt's and due to have the operation while we were on holiday in Malta, so we were very keen to follow her progress. She had kindly told Anna that we could visit her in August after several weeks had passed so we could ask her any questions we might have.

Neither Emma nor Ruth had other family members with scoliosis and this was the puzzling fact for Anna as well. I have eight nephews and nieces and all of them have straight spines. Most children are diagnosed (I have since found out) with what is termed idiopathic scoliosis, which basically means that the cause is not known, although it is thought that there may be a genetic link. I now really believe this theory because on that memorable holiday I also had the chance to check Matt's and Rachel's back as they were frequently in swimming costumes. The next chapter reveals what I saw.

The holiday overall was fantastic and we all returned refreshed and relaxed. Emma had successfully had her operation in July as planned and at the end of August Anna asked if we could visit.

She lived only five minutes away and on the journey we wondered how many other young people with scoliosis were living locally. Now that we knew about the condition, newspaper articles about it kept cropping up and friends all seemed to know someone with it, although before the diagnosis we didn't know anyone at all.

It was wonderful to see that Emma had come through the operation successfully and now had a much straighter spine. Apparently not all spines can be completely straightened but the aim is for the curvature to be reduced to between 10 and 20 degrees and Emma's now minimal curve was in this range. I have to admit to feeling quite disappointed at this news although I didn't voice this to Anna. I wanted Anna's back to be pin straight if she had to go through the trauma of surgery, and it made me hope even more that she wouldn't need the procedure at all.

Another surprising fact was Emma's scar; it formed a curve in her side rather than down her back. This meant Emma had needed to have a lung drained and a rib removed to perform the operation. Emma said that the rib was ground down and then sprinkled over the titanium pins and rod to fool the body into thinking these were part of the body and so help everything fuse well together. We learned that surgery could involve either this side incision or a posterior incision down the back alongside the spine itself. These were officially called 'anterior fusion' or 'posterior fusion' respectively, and a brief summary of what each entails is as follows:

Posterior fusion is where the surgeon will operate through the back with an incision straight down the back. A brace is not normally needed because rods, hooks and screws will hold the spine in place until full fusion is achieved.

Anterior fusion is where the surgeon will operate through the front or side, through the abdominal cavity, so that access to the front of the spine is made and bone-grafting screws and rods are used.

Emma looked really well, although very tired, and after just half an hour of talking to us needed to rest and lie down. We were just so pleased and grateful to have had this opportunity so close at hand and it was very reassuring to see someone post-surgery, everything having gone well. Anna and I now felt more optimistic about going to the next appointment and dealing with whatever news awaited us.

FOUR

An unexpected result

Our holiday in Malta had enabled me to look much more closely at Matt's and Rachel's backs (which had initially seemed very straight in the aftermath of Anna's diagnosis) as I naturally wanted to check both their spines immediately.

Matt is not a sun lover and doesn't particularly enjoy swimming, but he loves snorkelling and we had taken fins and masks with us in case an opportunity to snorkel arose. We were lucky enough to discover a wonderful, secluded bay where we could snorkel and swim mostly on our own, which gave me the perfect opportunity to watch Matt more closely. I noticed that when he walked, one side of his back just didn't seem right—somehow not exactly symmetrical, although I couldn't see his spine beneath the skin. When he bent over, his back did not seem even and flat all over. Andrew agreed that maybe something was not quite right and that we should get it checked out when we returned home.

Rachel adores swimming and I could see that fortunately her spine was completely straight (much to her relief and ours). I knew that if Rachel's spine was going to curve at all I would be able to identify it at the earliest possible stage because I was now so aware how changes can take place. I knew that I would definitely be checking her back very frequently once she started at middle school.

The GP appointment for Matt was duly made on our return and Matt cycled there on his own without any worries because he wasn't in any discomfort and we couldn't see or feel anything drastically abnormal. He came back with a referral to the consultant, just as a precaution because of Anna's diagnosis. The GP wasn't overly concerned and neither were we.

His appointment came through for October and I found myself now waiting with Matt in the orthopaedic outpatient clinic waiting to see the consultant once more. The x-ray had been taken without difficulty and we now waited calmly to see the results. Neither of us really expected to see a curve, so we chatted and relaxed amiably while waiting for the feedback.

Our names were finally called and after a brief discussion, the consultant turned his computer screen towards us, showing the x-ray of Matt's spine.

For the second time, in just a few months, I felt that terrible cold fear as I discovered that Matt also had idiopathic scoliosis. The evidence of the x-ray was indisputable and both Matt and I just stared in disbelief at the screen. We had been expecting a possible slight curve, but nothing had prepared us for a double curve or one that looked so pronounced. In fact, he had, to quote the official diagnosis: 'a thoracic left lumbar adolescent idiopathic scoliosis'. The thoracic curve to the right measured 31 degrees and the lumbar curve to the left measured 30 degrees. It looked like a reverse S and completely shocked us both.

Now I realised that there had to be a genetic link within our family; two children out of three with a specific diagnosis of scoliosis was surely more than just chance. I sincerely hoped Rachel would not develop the condition as well, although it was some reassurance to know that we would at least be more likely to spot any curvature early, possibly when Rachel would be only twelve or thirteen and so have it treated before the curve became as severe as Anna's. I later read that although scientists have known for years that scoliosis runs in families, its pattern of inheritance has remained unclear. That seems to be because the condition is most likely caused by several different genes that work in relation to one another (and the environment) to cause scoliosis.

Fortunately, the consultant was not too concerned about Matt, given that he had no pain or discomfort, and there was no disruption to his everyday life. However, he would need to be monitored as he hadn't yet reached his full growth potential, so a follow-up appointment and an x-ray was scheduled for the following August.

Now that I had two children with a confirmed diagnosis I started reading even further and tried to learn as much about the condition as I could. Some of the basic facts are:

- Scoliosis is a sideways curvature of the spine that makes the spine look more like an 'S' or 'C' than a straight 'I'.

- There are two types of scoliosis. Non-structural (mobile) scoliosis is usually caused by a condition outside the spine and disappears when that is corrected. For example, if one of your legs is longer than the other, the curvature in your spine will disappear when you sit down.

- Structural (true) scoliosis is a fixed curvature in the spine. Usually the underlying cause of structural scoliosis can't be treated.

- The first sign of scoliosis may be that clothes seem to hang unevenly, or when a parent or teacher notices a change in posture. Other signs may include one shoulder being higher than the other, or one shoulder blade sticking out. The space between the body and the arms may look different on each side when your child stands with their arms at their sides. One hip may be more prominent. A curvature can develop rapidly in children during growth spurts. A small curve may become a larger curve over a relatively short period.

- If the curve is in the upper back, the ribs may stick out on one side. This is known as a rib hump. Anna was very conscious of her 'hump' and as time progressed it made sitting on hard chairs very uncomfortable. Even watching a film at the cinema was hard by March 2011 because her hump was so prominent.

- Idiopathic scoliosis is a type of acquired scoliosis—in other words one not present at birth. 'Idiopathic' means an illness of unknown cause. The curvature with idiopathic scoliosis is almost always to the right, as was the case for Anna.

- Idiopathic scoliosis is quite common, affecting two to three in every 100 people. In eight out of ten cases the condition usually develops between the ages of 10 and 15, during the growth spurt of puberty. This is called late onset or adolescent idiopathic scoliosis. During adolescence, girls are much more likely to be affected than boys, probably because girls typically have shorter and faster growth spurts.

- Curves exceeding 20° occur in 0.3% to 0.5% of the population.
- Curves exceeding 30° occur in 0.2% to 0.3% of the population.
- Curves greater than 45° — 50° are usually treated surgically.

A good check for parents who are concerned that their child may be developing scoliosis is to ask them to stand in front of you and bend to touch their toes. Then step back from them and look at their back; if one side seems more raised than the other it could be that a curve is developing. When I asked Matt to do this, his back was only slightly uneven yet had a double curve of over 30 degrees to each side.

It was only a few weeks later that I opened the next appointment letter for Anna; November 15th was the date for the second x-ray. This was only four months after the first had been taken so we fervently hoped that there would be no change in the curvature. At this stage we were optimistic that the curve wouldn't worsen and we didn't particularly worry while waiting for the date to arrive.

FIVE

Did positive thinking help?

Between our initial appointment date in July and the next scheduled appointment in November, Anna had decided she would try positive thinking, plus daily stretching exercises to try to move her spine into a straighter position and at least halt any progression. I absolutely believe that positive thinking can lead to positive results so, with Anna's agreement, made a poster to put on the back of her door. This poster had the following three powerful statements which Anna believed in and declared several times daily:

- My back is straight
- My hip is straight
- I am strong and well

We both really believed that this could help, and as it couldn't possibly harm her, kept to it with enthusiasm. Neither of us wanted to seriously consider surgery at this point, and it was with fairly optimistic hearts that we returned to the Leicester Royal Infirmary on November 15th 2010 for the second x-ray. This time I waited anxiously because the results would decide whether or not surgery was needed.

Any hopes that Anna's back had remained unchanged were soon dashed when we saw the latest view of her spine. The curvature was actually significantly worse and now measured 55 degrees to the right. It was not good news and we both knew then that the likelihood of it worsening further as she continued to grow was a strong possibility—and more likely, a probability.

Again, we were rendered speechless for a few minutes as we tried to take in this new, unwelcome information. Our consultant now advised us that Anna should be put on the waiting list for surgery immediately, and recommended that she would be best with a 'posterior instrumental correction of scoliosis T2—L1', but the final decision would be made on the basis of 'bending' x-rays carried out at a pre-assessment.

It was a shock, but surprisingly not as great as when the curve was initially diagnosed, because I think we had both thought about the possibility of this scenario long before the appointment came through.

We now had to go home and wait for a date for surgery. Anna started to get increasing levels of discomfort in her back and had to take pain relief on most days. She also had to massage her back frequently while at school. In fact the hump on her back seemed to be getting more and more pronounced and made sitting at school very uncomfortable. She was also finding it harder and harder to perform all the movements she needed in her dance GCSE, although her teacher was very supportive and let Anna know that all the main practical elements could be completed in May 2012 when hopefully she would have had over a year to recover from surgery. She tried to reassure Anna and could not have been more helpful. Nevertheless it was a very difficult time.

Due to the difficulties Anna now had with dancing, she changed to a different dance school, one which developed drama and acting skills alongside street dancing. Anna hoped to return to ballet and modern dance in the future, but for now this seemed a good option and it would allow Anna to be entered for LAMDA (London Academy of Music and Dramatic Art) exams when she was ready.

She loved it all and was entered in her first exam for the following term. She prepared hard for it, delighting in presenting a monologue to the best of her abilities, and in January 2011 passed her Grade 5 exam; it was a wonderful achievement after all the anxiety about surgery.

It was nice, too, to have a positive event in January because we had also found out that, due to various administrative hiccups, Anna did not get put on the waiting list for surgery in November as promised, but on January 5th. This was a setback, particularly when we then heard via the consultant's secretary that an operation before the summer was unlikely. To the hospital system Anna was just a name, but to us it was Anna's world being held in limbo until something could be done.

By this time I was very concerned that her back would be a great deal worse by the summer, so we went back to see our GP to ask if she could write a letter to the consultant requesting an x-ray in March. This would be four months after finding out her curve had increased to 55 degrees, and the likelihood was that her back could be over 60 degrees by then. We hoped that she would be prioritised if her curve was thought to be more severe than others on the waiting list.

Our GP was wonderful, agreed with us that Anna needed an appointment before the summer, and sent a letter off to the consultant that week. We were very fortunate and within a fortnight we had another appointment, set for March 7th, for Anna's third x-ray and a discussion with the consultant who would also perform the surgery.

On the afternoon of the appointment I needed to pick Anna up from school early to make the 2.30pm time and I was running slightly late, which was very unusual for me given my clock-watching obsession! Consequently, when I heard the phone ringing just as I was shutting the front door, I hesitated and almost left it, thinking the answer machine would pick it up and I could deal with any messages that night.

Fortunately, I didn't leave it but rushed back to check that it wasn't urgent. I am so glad I made that decision because it was the scoliosis nurse at the Queen's Medical Centre (QMC) in Nottingham where Anna was due to have her operation. She was ringing to confirm various appointments for Anna that Thursday, March 10th at the QMC. When she heard that we hadn't been sent a letter she was alarmed (as was I) but very pleased that we could cancel other commitments and attend that week for various tests during the day. I would have dropped anything if it meant Anna would get the operation she needed so badly.

"Yes, we'll be there. Please just tell me where and when!"

I think someone was watching over me that day, making sure I answered that telephone call.

Anna needed to have various pre-tests done before the operation and I knew that once these were completed she would be in the system, and hopefully ready to have the operation itself. The scoliosis nurse agreed that once these tests had been done, an operation date should follow within a few months if not sooner.

Anna was already waiting for me when I pulled up outside the school several minutes later than planned, and I greeted her with the words, "Anna, you are never going to believe who I've just spoken to!" We both felt quite excited following the call!

This excitement vanished, however, when we received the results of the third x-ray. Anna's spine was now 66 degrees curved to the right. Since July the curvature had worsened by over 20 degrees.

Our consultant couldn't tell us when the operation would be; it was just a waiting game now and we simply had to wait for our turn. I felt helpless and extremely frustrated that I couldn't do anything to help Anna, but could only pray that Thursday, when we would be at the QMC for the pre-op tests, would be a positive step towards getting the operation done. It was very frustrating to know that something could be done, but not straightaway, and that we had no choice but to wait, all the time knowing that the curve was likely to be worsening with every passing week.

SIX

The pre-operation tests

Thursday, March 10th soon arrived and Anna felt pleased that she was missing an RE exam! but nervous about the day ahead. I was just pleased that we were moving further along the path to surgery.

The Queen's Medical Centre, in Nottingham, is an impressive building encompassing various blocks and different levels. Thankfully for me it was easy to find and even easier to park: a relief for both of us!

Our first appointment was in the Cardiology department for tests to check Anna's heart function and we needed to be in 'Cardiology South', D floor at 11.30am. As Anna's not keen on using lifts we walked up to the fourth floor but had to stop halfway because she was out of breath; it made me realise just how much her lung function had been compromised and I was interested to see how she would fare on the lung function assessment which was scheduled for the afternoon.

All the appointments throughout the day (five in total) ran smoothly, and on time, which was excellent. Her heart function tests were all normal as was the ECG (Electrocardiogram) test.

She then had to see the phlebotomist to give blood samples for other tests.

The nurse administering the lung function test was very kind and supported Anna as she measured her capacity for exhaling and inhaling air. Anna had to try and exhale sufficient air to make a spot on a computer screen rise and hit a target. Several times she almost succeeded, and she was successful once. She found it helpful to be receiving instant feedback from the computer. The inhaling task was easier for her. The nurse said her results were fine in terms of having the operation, although from her comments I suspected she was surprised Anna hadn't performed even better.

We then had an appointment with a scoliosis nurse who weighed Anna and took her blood pressure: all normal. She also gave us her email address at the hospital. This contact point was helpful and reassuring.

We had our final appointment of the day with the anaesthetist, who spent over half an hour talking Anna through what would happen on the day—how long the operation would last (between five and seven hours), what she could expect in terms of tubes attached to her, and how to manage her own pain relief when she woke up after the operation. She was careful to give Anna plenty of time to ask questions and process all the new information. She also commented on Anna's lovely straight white teeth (the braces had now been removed!) which was a positive boost for her.

We found out that the pain relief after the operation would come from intravenous morphine which would be controlled by pushing a button on a hand-held device. This was also when we learnt what T2 and L1 meant; that Anna would have a scar running from the second thoracic vertebrae down to the first lumbar vertebrae. I was relieved that she wouldn't need to have her lung drained for this particular type of incision and I hoped that she would still have enough flexibility for her to realise her dream of becoming a dancer.

I was told to prepare for Anna's face looking puffy after the operation due to fluid building up in her head, which was because she would be lying flat on her front for a long time without moving. This was to reassure me in case I worried the puffiness could have been due to a complication. She hastily added that Anna wouldn't have access to a mirror initially!

Anna learned that some monitors would be put on her scalp during the operation and was given the good advice of tying her hair into two plaits to minimise a 'bad hair day', which would be very important to any teenage girl, particularly as Anna wasn't going to be able to wash it for a few days.

We were told that she would be in the High Dependency Unit (HDU) for 1 night and then transferred to a ward or possibly a single room for the remaining 4-5 days. We would also need to come back to the QMC one final time before the operation day to have two important tests which had to be done as close to the actual operation date as possible. At this stage we didn't know what they would involve, only that one was connected to spinal monitoring and one involved x-ray bending films.

We would be sent an appointment once we had a confirmed operation date. Unfortunately, no-one could tell us when that might be but it was unlikely to be March or April, which was disappointing news because we had hoped it would be before Easter.

We both arrived home exhausted, but very pleased everything had run so smoothly and to know we were a step nearer the operation.

The very next day our scoliosis nurse rang us with brilliant news; we had a date! Anna would have her operation on Friday, May 6th. Exactly eight weeks to wait. Finally we could begin our countdown.

On March 22nd I received another email; the operation had been brought forward to April 29th; now we were only five weeks away.

The joy was short lived; the date was put back to May 6th. The hospital staff hadn't realised that the 29th was the date Prince William and Kate Middleton were due to get married so would be a public holiday, and operations would not be scheduled in. At least it was only a week's difference and anyway, we were looking forward to watching the royal wedding ourselves!

On April 4th I had confirmation by email of the final test dates. The last pre-op tests would be on April 14th. Anna also apparently needed to attend an extra appointment we had not been expecting, at the Children's Respiratory Unit on April 12th. This was with a respiratory professor and the referral had come from the anaesthetist following our appointment at the QMC in March. We knew that this appointment must relate to Anna's results on the lung function tests and I hoped desperately it wouldn't delay the operation itself.

SEVEN

Preparations

Now we could seriously begin thinking about what we would need to take to the hospital and any items we would need to support her at home, because we had been told that the appointment with the respiratory specialist should not affect Anna's operation date.

We had been recommended some good websites by our consultant and from these I learned that we should have a non-slip mat in the shower—vital, because a sudden slip could be damaging after such delicate surgery.

Anna was more concerned about how she would wash her hair, and 'dry shampoo' seemed a good solution. Then Emma emailed us to say she had been encouraged to get up and have a shower only a few days after the operation so we could take normal shampoo with us. I was amazed, but of course Anna would be encouraged to get mobile as soon as possible to minimise the chance of any blood clots, and to get all her muscles back to working normally as quickly as possible.

In fact, we were later recommended that Anna should not shower until at least fourteen days post-operatively, by which time the wound would have healed over. It was very important not to get the scar wet while it was still in the early stages of healing, because this could increase the likelihood of infection. I was very happy to comply with this, and even

Anna coped with not washing her hair for two weeks; after such a major operation the state of your hair, even in teenage girls, is not such a high priority after all!

I read that Anna might find lifting her arms above her head uncomfortable at first, so to take tops that buttoned up at the front and cardigans rather than jumpers. In fact she could wear baggy tops relatively easily, but the buttoned-up pyjama top was helpful and we wished we had purchased several instead of only one which then had to be washed periodically in hospital.

We also bought smooth jogging bottoms and loose-fitting trousers which were recommended rather than jeans, and finally, easy-to-slip-on shoes or slippers were needed because Anna apparently wouldn't be able to do shoes up for a while. (In actual fact, after the operation the physiotherapists recommended having shoes or sturdy slippers with a back to make it easier to walk steadily in the hospital).

We had already stocked up on some new release DVDs, and friends offered us their favourites. We especially favoured comedies as this would raise Anna's spirits and even add to the healing process. We didn't realise at this stage that Anna would need to have a costoplasty done during surgery, which meant four of her ribs had to be broken in order to reduce the prominence of the rib hump. This meant that laughing was very painful for a while afterwards and Anna had to hold her sides carefully. One of her frequent phrases was to be "Don't make me laugh, Mum".

One of Anna's favourite chocolates is pralines, so I knew that we would be stocking up on these as well, although Anna said she didn't want to leave hospital heavier than when she went in! I had no idea what her appetite would be like after the operation or indeed what the hospital food would be like, but I wanted to make sure we would have enough treats to get her through the first few days which I had read would be pretty painful and unpleasant.

In fact neither of us felt like chocolate at all during the hospital stay and Anna's favourite treats were a variety of smoothies and drinks to help wash down all the medication she needed. She also enjoyed sucking on orange segments and pineapple slices which were refreshing and didn't need to be eaten, because her appetite was very small for the first few days. The pralines were later brought home in a congealed lump due to the heat of the ward!

I optimistically packed four good books to read during 'spare' moments in hospital, which weighed down my bag but subsequently never got read because no 'spare' moments arose. A daily paper provided more than adequate reading material. I also took a towel for me to shower with, which again proved unnecessary because the hospital provided towels for parents if they were needed (which is not the case for all hospitals).

We were told that she would be allowed home when she was able to walk up and down the stairs, and she would be asked to do this in order to have a post-op x-ray taken before she could be discharged.

Another important issue before the operation was how the time off from school would affect Anna's GCSEs as there were five important exams in May and June. We knew she would have to miss at least two of these, but with the earlier operation date we were hopeful that she might be able to sit the remaining three. She would officially be allowed back into school after six weeks and then we would evaluate whether she could walk there or if we needed to arrange lifts. I wasn't sure how she would manage carrying her bags, but she had a very good support network of friends who I knew would help her.

We accepted that she might miss all the exams anyway because she would probably be too tired and in too much discomfort to revise for them. Either way, the school advised us to get a letter from our GP explaining Anna's situation and how missing some exams would be unavoidable. The school promised to support Anna in whatever way they could and asked me to ring, following the operation, to discuss any special needs she might have on returning to school. I also met or rang her teachers, who all wanted to support and help her as much as possible. They agreed to email work home to us when she was off and give us as much relevant and useful information beforehand as they could.

We would have to hope everything ran smoothly because it was impossible to fully anticipate what was going to happen.

EIGHT

The final tests

On April 12th Anna was ready to go back to the lung function clinic at QMC where she was seen by a respiratory professor who checked her lung function once more, just to be sure she would be fine during the operation.

The appointment ran smoothly and the professor felt that Anna was very fit for surgery in the near future because the lung function tests revealed only mild restriction consistent with the scoliosis. Her trachea was central and her chest clinically clear, which was good news. He was happy for surgery to proceed on the 6th May as planned.

Only two days later on April 14th Anna and I returned again to the hospital for the x-ray bending films plus the spinal monitoring test, and, finally, to meet with our consultant surgeon, to sign the surgery consent form.

The x-ray bending films were done first, and involved two x-rays where she stood upright before lying on a bed and having further x-rays taken while she bent her back to both the right and left sides while lying flat. This was to see how much flexibility there was in her spine and the position it was in for when they had to move it to a straighter position during surgery. The results of these were very positive, and despite the curvature in her spine being now 74 degrees, when she bent to one side the spine moved into an almost central position and our surgeon was fairly confident that he would be able to straighten it successfully. Nothing of course could be guaranteed, and it would not be known how easily the spine would move until the operation was underway.

The spinal monitoring test was done in the Clinical Neurophysiology department and had the official name of 'Pre-operative SEP investigation'. SEP stands for SomatoSensory Evoked Potentials. Evoked potentials are signals from the brain that are given out when it is stimulated by visual, auditory or sensory stimuli. In other words, signals given out as a result of the things you see, hear and touch. For this test the clinical physiologist only concentrated on Anna's arms and legs. During her surgery the staff would use these results as a reference.

The test itself took about an hour, although the nerve stimulation only took a few minutes for each point. Anna had to sit on a chair initially and have her head measured. Then precise marks were made on her scalp with a skin crayon. Each mark was rubbed gently with mild abrasive jelly before a small number of electrodes (little recording discs) were stuck to each mark.

That day a water-based paste was used which washed out easily, but during surgery a stronger glue would be used to ensure that none of the electrodes moved out of position during the operation. Electrodes were also stuck to the back of her neck, each side of her collarbone and behind her knees. Anna was told to wear her hair in two plaits to keep it out of the way as much as possible during the operation and make it easier for the electrodes to be glued to her scalp.

For the test itself, Anna was allowed to relax on a comfortable bed half sitting/half lying down. Then certain nerves in her arms and legs were tested .She said she felt a tapping sensation inside either her hands or feet, which wasn't painful but felt strange! She was glad she had worn loose-fitting leggings because these needed to be rolled above her knees so that the electrodes could be fitted correctly.

We were also asked if Anna could be photographed so that she would have 'before' and 'after' surgery pictures of the position of her spine and hips. These images would be part of her medical records. We also consented to them being used for teaching medical, paramedical and nursing staff as well as medical students in Nottinghamshire and other UK medical schools. They may also get presented at scientific meetings in the UK and abroad.

We then finally met our consultant to talk through the surgery and for me to give my written consent. Anna was in daily pain now so I knew we had no option but to consent to surgery because this was the only way she could live a normal life. We had to fill in a questionnaire relating to Anna's perception of how her back made her feel, how much pain she was in etc, and she ringed the highest number for most questions indicating significant pain and a desperate need to get back to normal. Nevertheless, signing a form which warns about possible unpleasant complications, is not enjoyable and my heart rate was significantly higher than usual.

Anna asked about how well she would be able to dance after surgery, but of course our surgeon couldn't fully answer that until after the rods and pins had been inserted. Because the rods would only go down as far as the first lumbar vertebra she was really hoping that her flexibility would be unimpaired. In the end the rods actually went from T3 (third thoracic vertebra) to L3 (third lumbar vertebra).

By the end of the day we both had a headache and felt

worn out. We had spent six hours sitting, waiting, being tested and discussing all aspects of the situation. We knew that next time we arrived in Nottingham it would be May 5th, the day before the operation which was due to start at around 7.30am on May 6th. We had to arrive by 5.30pm the day before.

Only three weeks to go. Anna was told to make sure she didn't get her back sunburnt before the operation and to try and stay as healthy as possible. The last thing we wanted was for her to be struck down by a horrible cold or virus.

The next day I received a call from Anna's school to say that having seen that Anna would be away for various GCSE exams, the school vice-principle had agreed that an exam invigilator could come to our house on the exam dates so that Anna could sit the tests under exam conditions in our house, if she felt well enough. She would even be allowed slightly longer to complete the tests so that she could take rest breaks whenever she needed to.

This was brilliant news because we had assumed that she would have to miss the exams completely. Of course, we knew that she might not feel well enough to revise for the exams, never mind sit them, but it was a new option and made Anna feel very supported and positive that the whole procedure might not be too problematic.

This was the last day of the Spring term so Anna now had two weeks at home to relax and revise as much as she could. The weather turned out to be glorious and she was able to relax and keep healthy. We even had a two-day break at Legoland, which was really good fun and helped distract us all from the operation ahead.

Looking at the photos afterwards made me realise how normal Anna still looked in her clothes, despite having such a severe curve. It made me appreciate how easy it is to miss a much less severe curve and consequently I did feel a little less negligent. After the holidays there was a bank holiday Monday, so then there were only two more school days until the 5th arrived.

Fortunately, she would be able to go to school on the day before the operation, which would help keep her mind occupied so she wouldn't have too much time to worry about what was ahead. I would be allowed to have a bed next to her throughout the hospital stay, which was a reassuring thought for both of us.

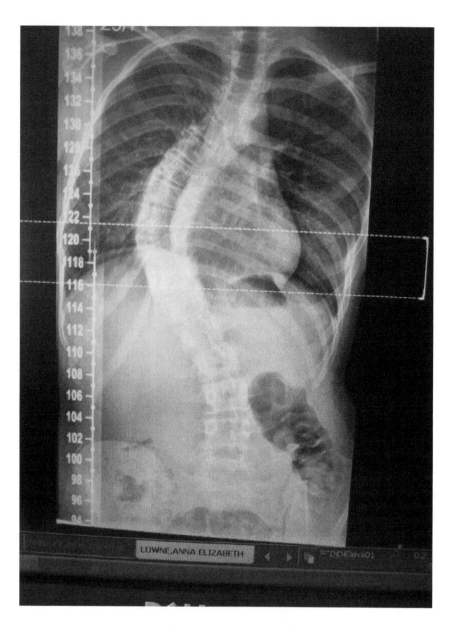

Pre-op x-ray showing 74 degree curve

NINE

The day before the operation

Finally May 5th arrived and we all woke up fairly nervous about the events that would take place over the next 48 hours. Anna went off to school as usual, feeling more excited than nervous because she now so desperately just wanted her back to be straight.

We had both packed our bags the previous night. I had a rucksack containing enough clothes for a week, which was hopefully the longest time we would be in hospital, and a small holdall which was full of books, DVDs, chocolate pralines and other tasty treats. This weighed far more than the rucksack, and between us (Anna had her laptop packed and a holdall with clothes, hair-dryer etc) we looked as if we were setting off on a mini-break holiday, and it caused some hilarity as we loaded up the car.

Rachel was at a friend's house and Matt had a late finish from school so Andrew, Anna and I left the house with little ceremony, feeling nervous and strangely excited that the operation was so imminent.

En-route, Anna chatted about the prospect of having a single side-room with an en-suite shower, which is the facility Emma, Matt's friend, enjoyed after her spinal surgery. In our mind's eye we envisaged the light airy room and the space and privacy a single room would bring.

The traffic into Nottingham was slow-moving in the rush

hour and felt like any other working day; the thought of the operation was being blocked out by all of us. Most of the journey was spent in silence as we listened to the radio.

We had been told to arrive at Ward D34 by 5.30pm and it was only shortly after that when Andrew drove up and parked in front of the main East Block entrance. This was the first stage. He walked with us to the main lifts before saying goodbye and giving Anna a big hug with lots of reassurances about well everything would go. He looked as nervous as we both now felt, and as he disappeared round the corner we both took a deep breath as the anticipation and enormity of the operation hit us.

I couldn't imagine how Anna was feeling because I felt sick at the thought of what she had to go through. Outwardly she seemed perfectly at ease, but I knew she was very anxious. Her main fear was of being paralysed after surgery or waking up during the procedure, but she didn't voice these now as we waited for the lift.

It was good to know that the two of us would be there together throughout the entire stay. I was so relieved that parents were welcomed and in fact encouraged to stay with their children if they needed the support.

We duly arrived at the ward but found that a bed wasn't yet ready so had to wait in the playroom area while a bed in a bay of four was prepared. The ward was noisy and bright with children talking loudly and nurses busily moving from task to task. As we sat precariously on tiny, red plastic chairs with a children's television programme blaring out from the playroom's television, Anna's face told a thousand words. No single room and the possibility of sharing a bay with babies in cots? This was not a good moment and the thought of staying there for a week seemed daunting, even without the surgery being thrown in.

However, after half an hour a bed was ready and we found that her bay was temporary home to another teenage girl and two younger girls (but thankfully not babies, who inevitably are often very noisy little people!) and actually felt very welcoming and bright.

The three other girls were also accompanied by their mums for their stay in hospital and all of them were so welcoming and friendly that it felt like an immediate support network. They told me where to get the fold-up beds, clean linen and towels from, and when breakfast would be available, plus all the other essential bits of information needed to help us through the stay.

We both agreed that it was possibly better than having a single room because it was reassuring to feel part of a group and have other people around who would support us from a parent/patient perspective rather than the professional view of the nurses, despite them all being absolutely fantastic throughout the very long days that followed, and who answered all Anna's questions that evening brilliantly.

We decided that we should watch a DVD to pass the time. This, however, was almost a disaster because the background music was quite loud and scary throughout and not appropriate for the two younger girls in the bay. Luckily, Anna had packed her head-phones which we could share, and so enjoy the film knowing that everyone else wasn't subjected to it as well!

After we had eaten some tea the evening passed quite uneventfully until nine o'clock when all the main lights went off and we were plunged into darkness. Not a power cut, as we immediately wondered, but the time when everyone is supposed to go to sleep! All the parents looked at each other (it was everyone's first night) and saw the comical side as we all now had to set up our beds and get changed etc in very subdued lighting. We would be prepared for the next night!

Anna was allowed to eat and drink normally up until midnight and then 'nil by mouth' until after surgery. The nurses had told her that she would be woken at 5am for a small glass of water and have anaesthetic cream put on the back of her hand where the initial anaesthetic would be inserted. This can take a couple of hours to work so she would be allowed to go back to sleep until 7am.

Anna seemed to suddenly grasp the enormity of the situation and realise that the operation was now very near. Her biggest worry was still whether or not she would wake up during the operation, because she knew some patients had to be brought out of the anaesthetic slightly so they could answer questions or instructions such as 'wiggle your toes' to check that the nerves in the spine were still working correctly.

She was also very anxious that she would feel pain during the operation. I could sense her anxiety and hoped that my answers and reassurances helped; we were essentially optimistic and positive, but when we both signed the consent form in April we knew that, as unlikely as it was, things could go wrong during surgery because of its invasive nature, and it was certainly a procedure not without risk.

We both tried to get a few hours' sleep and not dwell too much on the morning ahead.

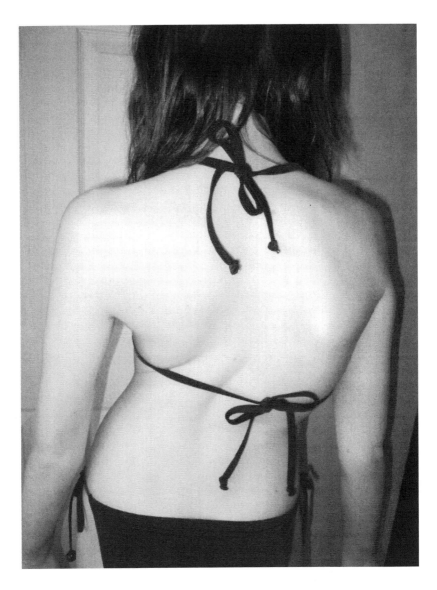

Anna's back the day before surgery

TEN

The Operation

Needless to say neither Anna nor myself slept well that night and both of us were awake well before the nurse arrived with the anaesthetic cream. Anna was calm but very nervous now about the operation.

Her main worry regarding whether or not she would need 'the wake up test' during the operation was put to the anaesthetist when he came to us at 7am. This test is only necessary in around 1 in 300 spinal operations and involves the anaesthetist reducing the amount of anaesthetic so if Anna was asked to move her toes during the op she would be able to do so without being conscious of moving them. Quite a scary thought, although she wouldn't be able to remember the event afterwards.

Of course, she was reassured by the anaesthetist that she would not feel any pain at all and would certainly not 'wake up'. The anaesthetist was very professional and calming, answering Anna's last-minute questions without making her feel rushed.

At 7.45am she was wheeled down to the anaesthetic room, which was just outside the theatre where her operation would take place. She spoke to our consultant before he had changed into his surgical gown, and met the small team of people who would be involved. I was the observer now and could only wait next to Anna while she answered questions (she became very quick at giving her name and date of birth over the next few days!) and was put at her ease by staff. I held her hand and waited with her.

By 8am Anna was ready to have the first anaesthetic, which would put her to sleep. She queried what would happen if she didn't fall asleep but was told, with a reassuring smile from the anaesthetist, that she would make medical history if she didn't fall asleep; the anaesthetist always wins!

It was a strange situation, waiting directly outside the theatre in this small room, surrounded by various medical staff, all of us waiting for the moment when the surgery could begin. Time seemed to slow down. Everyone tried to make Anna feel relaxed, chatting to her about school and the hobbies she enjoyed.

The distractions worked and it was only a few minutes later that I gave Anna a final kiss and left the room to the reassuring words of 'Don't worry, we'll take good care of her'. I took a deep breath; I knew I couldn't do anything now except wait. I prayed to all the angels to watch over her and it took huge effort to keep my emotions in check as I walked back to the ward. The other mums gave me a big hug because they had all been in a similar position over the previous days, and luckily for them they were all due to head for home later that day. The camaraderie and support from other parents on the ward was something I hadn't expected but was extremely grateful for.

I knew I couldn't stay around the hospital all day because our surgeon had prepared me for not hearing from the team until at least 5pm when hopefully Anna would be regaining consciousness in the recovery room.

I had over eight hours to wait.

I was very lucky; less than ten minutes walk from the hospital was the beautiful building, Wollaton Hall, set in fabulous gardens and lawns. I walked down the avenue of lime trees up to the Hall in brilliant sunshine. The warmth helped to keep my spirits high and I felt surprisingly calm and relaxed as I walked and walked. I love being outside amid trees and greenery anyway so I couldn't have been in a better place. Many of the parents catch a bus into Nottingham while they wait, but I knew I didn't want the hustle and bustle that would bring, and the calm beauty in those grounds kept me focused and steady.

Texts from friends flooded in throughout the morning and all the support kept me buoyant. I even managed to have some lunch in the sunny courtyard, but by early afternoon I felt I needed to be back in the hospital just in case a call came earlier than expected for me to see Anna. I felt I could be more supportive to her by being physically nearer, and I was now happy to wait in the ward.

I had spoken to Andy at various times during the day and he was waiting equally anxiously while trying to work.

5pm came round eventually and from then onwards every minute seemed endless because I was clock watching continuously. I checked with the nurses twice that they knew where I was and continued to wait in the now empty bay, flicking through television channels but unable to concentrate on anything.

Finally, at 5.30pm our surgeon himself appeared round the corner with the wonderful, much awaited news that the operation had gone well, technically everything had gone to plan, he was pleased with the results and was confident that I would be too. I could have hugged him with relief but instead managed to shake his hand, smiling and thanking in equal measure.

"Can I see her now?" was my first request, but although Anna was in recovery there had been a slight problem in that she had developed an air bubble (technically called a small pneumothorax developed intra-operatively) and they were just waiting to see whether it would disappear on its own or would need a chest drain inserting; but I was assured that I would be able to see her very soon.

The consultant had not needed to authorise the 'wake-up test' (Anna could move her fingers and toes well—what a relief!) but had needed to do the costoplasty which involved breaking some of her ribs to enable the rib hump to go down better, which would obviously be a great improvement cosmetically. I was told that I could see Anna in the High Dependency Unit (HDU) in around 40 minutes, so only a short wait left. The consultant then left to check on Anna's progress and I texted Andy with the good news.

An hour passed and I felt the anxiety growing again as no call to go to HDU came. At long last, at 7pm, a nurse came to say Anna was now in the HDU and had been asking for me. It was only a short walk to the next floor and five minutes later I was next to her. I was so relieved that after all the worry everything was going to be ok.

I had expected various tubes to be attached to her, so this wasn't a shock, and she also had an oxygen mask on to help eradicate the unwanted air-bubble. She briefly opened her eyes and it was the most fantastic feeling to have her back. Talking was difficult because of her broken ribs and the lingering anaesthetic, but she managed to whisper 'I'm glad you're here'.

After all the months of waiting and worrying it was finally over. Now the recovery and slow journey back to normality could begin.

When we were home the following week I tried to find out exactly what a costoplasty is. Another name for this surgical procedure is thoracoplasty and it aims to reduce the rib hump that affects most scoliosis patients with a thoracic curve. It involves the removal or resection of several (in Anna's case, four) segments of adjacent ribs that protrude, each segment being 1-2 inches long.

The surgeon had asked for our permission to do the costoplasty if needed because we didn't want Anna to have to go through a second operation after the spinal fusion; far better to have both procedures done at once with only one general anaesthetic and only one scar.

ELEVEN

Day 1, Post-op: Saturday

Because of all the wires and machines attached to her I couldn't sleep next to Anna, but was allocated a parent's room a short walk away. This was quiet and restful and I was quite sure I would sleep well now that the operation was over. I had my mobile switched on and Janet, the named nurse in the HDU, had assured me that she would ring if Anna wanted me, although I had already said I would be back in the Unit by 7am if not earlier.

Of course, I now had new worries on my mind; the surgeon had had to put the rods as low as L3. Would this affect her flexibility and mobility? Would the air bubble disappear? Would her breathing be ok? How much pain would she be in? So despite my peaceful surroundings I was still awake at 2am, and by 6.30am had showered ready to return to the HDU.

What a difference less than 12 hours had made! Her face was less puffy and she was awake. She smiled as soon as I entered and asked 'Where have you been?'

The nurses were changing shifts and the day nurse, Jan, introduced herself to me and said how pleased she was with Anna's progress. She was breathing more easily and could speak audibly in short bursts. We could have a conversation and Anna was surprised that she had had a short conversation with me the previous night, because she had no memory of having seen me! Twice during the night she had even asked the nurses whether or not she had in fact *had* the operation! She couldn't believe the length of her operation because she felt that it had been like blinking; she had been awake pre-op then suddenly she was post-op. I had told her beforehand that it might feel like that, but Anna wouldn't believe me until she had experienced the sensation first hand.

This first day after surgery she was incredibly thirsty and was relieved that she could suck refreshing cordials from a straw if this was held to her lips. She couldn't really move because of the stiffness she now felt in her back, but was told a chest x-ray would need to be done that morning to check that the air bubble was decreasing so wouldn't cause any further problems.

The back of the bed would need to be raised gradually until it was almost upright so that her chest was in the correct position. The nurses moved the bed slightly more upwards every fifteen minutes and I could see Anna holding onto the bed rails anticipating it to hurt. In fact she moved the short distances quite easily and soon she was in the proper position.

Fortunately, the x-ray machine was portable so could be brought to Anna's bed, and the necessary pictures were taken before midday. I was allowed to see the results on the screen and they showed that, thankfully, the air bubble had virtually gone. Previously all the x-rays I had seen of Anna's spine showed it curved, but now I could see that it was virtually completely straight. She had 2 rods stretching from T3, the third thoracic vertebra, to L3, the third lumbar vertebra, plus 15 pins to secure them in place. It was incredible, and I marvelled at the expertise of our surgeon and all his team to make something so amazing happen. I felt so grateful and so happy that the invasive surgery was over; it was a wonderful feeling.

I relayed the good news to Anna, who was unable to relish my joy at this point, because the stiffness and discomfort were at the forefront of her mind and she had just heard that a physiotherapist would be arriving at the HDU within an hour to help her sit up for the first time and this had immediately filled her with panic at what lay ahead. It's very important to get patients mobile as soon as possible to speed up recovery, and I had noticed she was wearing tight stockings which went up to her mid-thigh to minimise the chance of blood clots in her legs. ,

The physiotherapist duly arrived and gave Anna some breathing exercises to try and do for a few minutes every hour to help get the lungs opening well (quite painful due to the healing ribs) and she should press the morphine button beforehand to keep on top of any pain.

She also announced that she and Jan would help Anna into a sitting position by swinging her legs over the side of the bed. This seemed an unrealistic goal so soon after such major surgery but I watched, amazed, as with great skill they helped her sit up for a few minutes. She felt quite dizzy and light-headed, but it was the first step along the recovery journey and something she could build on with every passing day.

The short burst of energy needed for this task completely exhausted her and she sank back onto the pillows relieved that she wouldn't need to exert herself too much again that day.

By lunchtime Anna was washed, in her own pyjamas and looking more like her old self, and even she was amazed when I told her it had been less than 20 hours since she had first been wheeled into the recovery room. The bright new pyjamas bought in preparation for the hospital stay were disappointing because when Jan and Beth, the nurses, dressed her, all the buttons dropped off. We should have invested in better quality! Luckily, Beth cheerfully presented me with a sewing kit and I was able to carefully sew them all back while Anna was sleeping. Unfortunately she was then sick all over them (and me) so finished off the day back in a hospital gown! We laughed about that incident later on; it helped to lighten Anna's mood throughout each day although she wasn't able to laugh easily because of the pain in her ribs.

Morphine provided wonderful pain relief but had the side effects of making Anna feel sick and suffer from itchiness all over her skin. I spent the first few days while she was on this medication carefully scratching areas of her back, legs and arms which she couldn't reach. She informed me that my nails could do with being longer and sharper!

The oxygen mask was removed by 1pm and replaced by a small nasal tube inserted just inside her nostrils, but easily removed. As time progressed she only needed this during sleeping when her breathing naturally became more shallow.

Throughout the day Anna gradually became more practised in moving the top part of the bed up or the lower part down in order to keep herself comfortable. The remainder of the day was spent resting, and culminated in a late night move at 10.30pm back to Ward D34.

The night was then punctuated by the nurses giving Anna regular checks and medication. The hope was that after a few days she wouldn't need the morphine but could switch to codeine, which doesn't have as many negative side-effects. So much had happened; it was hard to believe we were only one day after the operation.

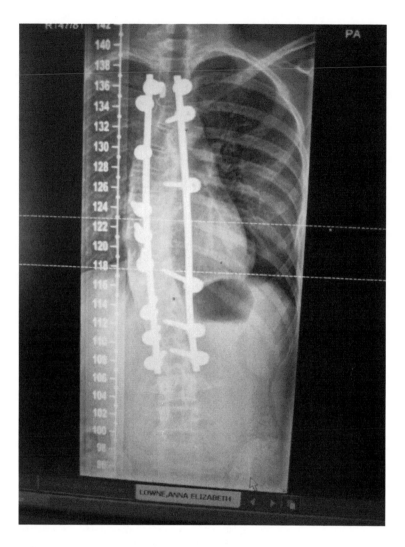

The rods and pins in Anna's back the day after surgery

Being on the ward again meant that I was able to set up a fold-up bed next to Anna. Our relationship over the week became much closer; she needed me 24/7 and became slightly anxious if I left her even for a few minutes. When I went to buy a paper or make a cup of tea in the little ward kitchen she wanted to know exactly how long I'd be, and preferred me not to go anywhere.

It was distressing for me to see her in so much pain (from the costoplasty more than the spine at times) and frustrating for Anna at how little she could do for herself, but it made us focus on the positive times ahead. We took strength in knowing that each little step forward was a step in the right direction.

TWELVE

Day 2, Post-op: Sunday

Anna managed to sleep reasonably well that night but needed help turning throughout the day in order to minimise the likelihood of bedsores. She could bring her knees up fairly easily and manage to move her shoulders a small amount, which helped her feel a bit more independent because otherwise she relied on me, and sometimes nurses as well, to try and move her slightly up or down the bed to get more comfortable. I knew how hard it was for her to be in bed for the majority of the day, and being in bed and unable to move as well was doubly frustrating for a young, active teenager.

She always needed to use the morphine before the enthusiastic physiotherapist arrived with activities for Anna to do, and we would always look out for her arriving on the ward each morning and guess how long it would be before she arrived at Anna's bed.

The first exercise that day was to consolidate her breathing, repeating the initial exercises from the previous day which aimed to open up her lungs more fully each time she did the exercise. It sounds fairly easy but in reality was a big challenge for Anna; she didn't particularly enjoy the effort and I had a fair amount of both cajoling and praising to do.

The second big aim for the day was to help Anna up into a standing position, which seemed like an incredible feat only two days after surgery. The two physiotherapists, always helpful and encouraging in their approach, reassured Anna that she couldn't possibly do any damage to her spine and, as they stood on either side of her, gently supported her into a standing position.

Wow, it was amazing to see her standing straight for the first time in many months. She was very stiff, but I saw a gleam of satisfaction and relief in her eyes as she realised that she could do it and that this was only the beginning of her recovery. She complained that her back felt very heavy and stiff, but of course all her muscles on one side had been suddenly stretched into the correct position. The rod and pins added to the rigid feeling which we were told was normal at this stage and should disappear as all her muscles began working normally again.

Her eyes met mine and she smiled as we both realised that she was now taller than me. "Mum, you're so small," she managed to whisper! It was wonderful to be able to smile with her rather than see her pain and try not to reflect it in my face. Achieving that wonderful target exhausted her and she followed it up with a well-earned rest.

Andrew and Rachel visited later in the afternoon, which was a fantastic mood lifter for Anna. Just to see them boosted her visibly despite not being able to make much conversation herself. They had brought more get-well cards with them and each thoughtful comment inside reminded Anna that all her friends and family were behind her every step of the way and wanted to help in whatever way they could.

As all good hospital visitors do, the two of them had bought in a selection of chocolates which could be put in the ward fridge, although the quantity was significantly depleted by Rachel who managed to eat most of the delicious-looking treats during the visit! However, in fairness to her, this was partly due to the fact that she was visibly shocked by the sight of her older sister looking unusually fragile and dotted with various drains and tubes. She spent most of the time talking to me and telling me about all the events at school and home. Anna was happy to lie back and listen to us all talking.

She was now able to drink more fluids during the day without feeling waves of nausea wash over her, but was very pleased that the catheter remained in place as it would have been an impossible task to rush to the toilet.

I was aware that Anna felt her progress was very limited and I had to remind her of the little things she could do which had seemed impossible only the previous day. Another girl, Alex, had had the same operation a few days earlier and was now walking up and down the ward, gently supported by her Mum or Dad, a few times each day. However, after talking to her mum, I discovered that she had not needed the costoplasty procedure that Anna had had, so didn't feel so much discomfort just breathing and moving. Anna was having to deal with two major operations at the same time, which I think even the nurses sometimes forgot. However, each day during the hospital stay, and at home later, brought new successes, albeit little ones, but each step could be built on and our continual focus was to keep looking forwards.

THIRTEEN

Days 3 - 6, Post-op

Another day dawned and I wondered what new challenge the physiotherapists would expect Anna to be able to strive for. I know Anna waited with some apprehension for the twice-daily visit because every movement was difficult, mainly due to the rib pain, but today the goal she achieved was to sit up, move to standing and walk three paces to a chair next to the bed where she could sit down for a few minutes.

The few minutes sitting increased to fifteen and what an achievement it felt. Despite the exhaustion even Anna managed to raise a small smile of satisfaction. She then managed to repeat this whole exercise in the afternoon, which helped build up her stamina and kept her focused on building up her mobility.

She was also able to shuffle slightly from side to side in the bed and put her knees up but couldn't yet push herself up the bed at all, which was very frustrating for her as she seemed to slide down the bed every few minutes. She then required me, and a nurse if possible, to help pull her up the bed. This pattern was repeated regularly throughout the day and the nurses were always incredibly kind and sympathetic.

The catheter was still in place and her appetite was still very small, but she enjoyed lots of different drinks; we found that smoothies were best for swallowing paracetamol, juices for the other tablets, and water in between.

We then had an unexpected visit on the third day from the hospital teacher, Kate, who came to let us know that she would be contacting Anna's school and the Home Education Service who should be able to put some home tuition in place so Anna would be better able to keep up with all her schoolwork. "She may be able to access between 5 and 10 hours' tutor time a week, and hopefully we'll hear within the next couple of weeks about the level of provision available," she said. Kate was a very cheerful, sparkly person with short, red spiky hair, who contributed to cheering Anna up even though the topic of conversation was schoolwork!

On Day four, Tuesday, Anna had the catheter taken out; no more plastic tubing getting wrapped around her legs! This was a great step forward and meant that Anna was now motivated to persevere with her walking so that she could manage the short walk to the toilet with me by her side every step of the way; she still felt quite light-headed and dizzy when she was walking, probably because most of her day was still spent lying down, but this would gradually change over time.

Another first today was Anna managing to get out of bed and sit in the chair to eat breakfast, her first proper breakfast since the operation, and it was good to sit opposite her rather than perched on the side of her bed or in a chair next to her, and see her appetite gradually returning.

Her spine still felt stiff and sore but our spinal nurse reassured her that daily movements were good and she couldn't do any harm to herself or damage any of the surgeon's good work. This was a reassurance Anna needed many times during her recovery because her new back still felt very strange.

Today, too, Anna's bed was moved into a new bay with other teenagers, which was a better environment for her as it meant being away from the lovely, but very noisy at night, babies who had had cleft palate repairs. Alex, the other fifteen-year-old girl who also loved dancing and who had had the same spinal surgery but without the costoplasty, three days before Anna, was motivating to watch and compare progress. Needless to say, the two girls exchanged details so they could keep in touch over the coming weeks.

The final good news of the day was that the morphine was taken away. The downside to this was that the strongest pain relief had gone, but the upside of less nausea and itching all over her body made it very worthwhile. Other pain relief took its place, of course, and this would also be gradually reduced as the days continued.

On Day five, Wednesday, Anna was able to sit in her chair for each meal during the day. She was eating well and finding it easier to do the manoeuvres needed to get from bed to chair and back again with minimal discomfort. This, combined with walking to the toilet several times a day, led to periods of tiredness and she needed to ensure that she rested throughout the day.

The big goal in the afternoon was a visit to the x-ray department to have an x-ray of her whole back while standing. I presumed that she would be taken by a porter but, after speaking to the nurses, realised that it would be me who would be responsible for making sure Anna got there safely. Anna was as apprehensive as I was before we started our journey because we both knew that we would have to negotiate lifts and corridors at a busy time of day.

The mode of transport was a solid wheelchair that had

wheels far more obstinate and immovable than any awkward shopping trolley you may have encountered at the local supermarket! I was advised to pull her backwards as the wheels went more smoothly, but combined with the fact that Anna couldn't see where she was going and thus felt nauseous, and with me having to twist half my body round in order to check I wasn't about to crash into an unsuspecting patient/visitor, meant it didn't look as though it was going to be a successful expedition.

So, against all good advice, once out of sight of the ward I endeavoured to heave Anna and chair the correct way round. As long as the wheels were pointing in the right direction and we travelled extremely slowly, we were able to make enough progress to complete the journey. Hopefully, we would be able to view the results with our scoliosis nurse later that day back on the ward, via one of the computers.

The last new event in the day was Anna having the dressing on her back changed; I watched the procedure very carefully knowing that the next time this was done I would be in charge! The wound itself looked amazingly neat and very straight. Small steri-strips covered the red scar line which fortunately I was advised to leave alone; they would come off over time. The hardest part for Anna was having the dressing removed because the surrounding part was very sticky like a huge plaster. Anna had never been a 'rip off all in one go' person so it was a slow process, particularly as every pull seemed to affect the pain level she felt in her ribs and shoulders, which also ached most days.

We had been told to keep the wound clean and dry, so no showers until at least two weeks had passed, by which time the wound should have healed over completely. Even

Anna was now happy to leave her hair, which actually didn't seem to change over the week anyway as she could tie it in a pony tail, because the thought of the wound getting wet and possibly infected was a guaranteed deterrent.

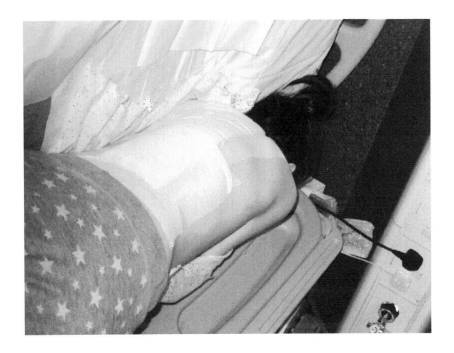

Having the dressing changed

Day six after surgery, Thursday, dawned with the fantastic realisation that we would be going home that evening. We were so looking forward to being able to see the outside world properly again rather than the varying blue or grey skies from the hospital windows, and the thought of being able to sleep in our own beds was a very pleasing prospect. It had seemed as though we had spent many more than seven nights in the hospital and we were both filled with excitement.

We had seen the latest x-rays and were delighted at Anna's new look: a straight back. It seemed so incredible and definitely worth every minute of stiffness and pain (although Anna possibly didn't agree with such vehemence as me at this point). The two rods and fifteen pins looked quite scary but were doing a very important job, and Anna had been told that she shouldn't be able to feel them at all in time. She had, however, noticed that she had altered sensation on her skin in various parts of her body, but we hoped that this was the result of the surgery and would only be temporary. Anna said the skin on her left leg and part of her chest felt much thicker than usual and she couldn't feel sensations properly, although she could walk and could move her toes and feet.

There was just one final hurdle to overcome before we could be discharged and that was completing the 'stairs test'. The physiotherapist had to check Anna could go up and down stairs before she was allowed home, so we duly walked to the stairs outside the ward, and to Anna's surprise (she thought that this would be too challenging) she passed with flying colours.

She had to take each step carefully and had to place both feet on one step before climbing up to the next one. Each step took a huge amount of strength and energy on Anna's part but was immensely satisfying for her. We were also given a wonderful purple beanbag we called 'heatie' which was a long, wheat-filled bag which could be warmed in the microwave and held against Anna's ribs and sides to relieve some of the discomfort. This worked brilliantly and we wished we had been given this earlier in the week. We were allowed to take it home, and over the next few weeks and even months, it was very helpful.

I was given enough dressings to last a couple of weeks and the medication needed for the initial ten days after we got home. Suddenly, we found ourselves ready to go, and now just had to wait for Andy to pick us up that evening.

We were wondering how slowly the afternoon would pass, but then had an unexpected visit from an undergraduate medical co-ordinator who was selecting patients willing to be part of 4th year medical student practical exams. This was for the students who had completed their paediatric placement and needed to pass a practical exam relating to a patient. Anna immediately agreed to be part of the exam and our slot was allocated for 1.10pm. Paul, our student, was excellent. Needless to say we tried to be as helpful as possible in answering his questions. Anna was suddenly a little apprehensive about taking part but was warmed by his proficient skills, and we both hoped that he passed with flying colours.

We still had a few spare hours so decided to tackle Anna's hair! The nurses kindly gave us a shower cap filled with special materials which, when warmed in the microwave, would 'wash' her hair. It sounded perfect but in fact failed to get put to use because it was too hard to put securely on Anna's head without it pulling on her neck and hurting her, so had to be fairly quickly abandoned. Alex had managed to use it successfully but it wasn't going to work for Anna.

She then decided that if we got some of the glue out that was left on her scalp from the various electrodes that were glued there for monitoring purposes during the operation, she would be able to brush her hair through. I managed to obtain some acetone and cotton wool balls, again from the nurses' store, and we were ready.

I had naively thought how easy it would be to remove the remaining glue, but again our plans were thwarted. I managed to get some of the glue off but most of it was firmly stuck and we had to be content with a half-completed effort. My brushing was apparently too gentle so Anna decided she could do better, grabbed the brush and began sorting her hair quite deftly. We then realised how well she was lifting her arms—right over her head—when the physiotherapist had been unable to persuade her to lift her arms to shoulder height that morning! Anna suddenly realised what she was doing and we both burst out laughing, although Anna's laughing was tempered by her rib pain and she had to hold her sides. "Don't make me laugh" was a familiar refrain over the next two weeks.

Anna could at last get changed into 'outdoor' clothes in preparation for the journey home. She had worn pyjama shorts for the past week and was ready for a change! She was giving a chirpy thumbs-up for a photo which showed the progress she had made in only a week, when we had a call from Andy to say he was only five minutes away. We were ready and waiting. I remembered to ask Andy to bring a wheelchair up from reception so we could be saved from the ordeal of the ward wheelchair again. It felt quite sad to be saying goodbye to the wonderful staff and children still remaining on the ward, but the excitement ahead outweighed any nostalgic feelings.

Finally, we were in the car, leaving our hospital home. The staff had been brilliant and we had had gold standard care, but we were delighted at the prospect of finally heading back to Leicester, Anna with pillows and cushions carefully propped around her to support her back comfortably before

Andy drove us safely back home. It was a fantastic feeling to see the fields and trees speed past us as we both looked forward to being back home.

FOURTEEN

Week 2

Rachel and Matthew were watching out for us and came out to greet the three of us, smiling expectantly. Matt hadn't seen Anna at all since surgery and he looked taken aback at how gingerly she moved. I hastened to reassure him that it was the costoplasty after-effects which made movements particularly cautious, and her back itself was becoming gradually less stiff with each day. I knew that Matt was aware that he could need surgery one day in the future to correct his own scoliosis.

Despite the fact that I had to set the alarm clock for three tablet-taking slots, I slept fairly well our first night and Anna too was glad to be in her own bed, although she had to adapt to a completely flat bed without the side rails to use as leverage which she had had in hospital. We had a torch in her bedroom alongside the pill packets and the times when she was due to take each particular tablet. This routine worked well and took us successfully to midway through the second week when she needed me less in the night and could manage her own pain relief successfully.

Once downstairs, Anna spent the days sitting in the armchair, supported by cushions and pillows, or lying on the settee with similar props. She was able to do physiotherapy exercises on her bed first thing in the mornings and downstairs in the afternoons. Anna was very keen to do the exercises twice daily as instructed because she was determined to get the maximum flexibility back in her spine.

It was frustratingly slow progress initially, but as the week progressed became less of a chore as Anna could see the progress she was making in terms of strength, stamina and flexibility. I had given her a little bell to ring if she needed me when I was briefly out of the room. This worked well in the day and also at night if she woke and needed help turning or manoeuvring, although I was very pleased not to hear it ring too frequently!

One afternoon, even Rachel rang the bell rather cheekily to see if I could get her a drink and snack while she was watching television!

On the Saturday of the second week Anna walked into our bedroom unaided and on Sunday managed to bend at her hips to pick fallen objects from the floor in her bedroom, although I noticed that this skill didn't seem to have transferred to the lounge when the television remote fell on the floor, or indeed to the lower kitchen cupboard for squash in order to make herself a drink. The bell still jangled loudly for my services!

By Monday she could walk up and down the stairs normally and could lie on her front during the night if she wanted. Tuesday was spent in the same routine of physiotherapy exercises, TV and resting, followed by more physiotherapy exercises later in the day. Together we watched numerous films (a kind friend had delivered a bag of DVDs to keep Anna occupied) and endless house restoration and design programmes!

Fortunately, Anna could see the television from her lying-down position, but it meant the days passed fairly slowly and by the evening she was wishing she had a wider range of movements. It was refreshing for her when Rachel and Matt returned from school just because there were more distractions and it helped to relieve the boredom of the day. Progress was frustrating in that it couldn't be hurried and we just had to wait for time to pass.

By Wednesday, Anna was able to wash and change her top without my help, which boosted her confidence. It was good to see her independence returning slowly. She still complained that her left thigh and part of her right side hadn't got normal sensation back and felt very strange to her touch, but we hoped this would decrease as she recovered.

She also complained that the pain in her ribs seemed to be worsening and she found it harder and more painful to breathe properly. This increased during the day until by late afternoon both of us were starting to feel quite anxious. Not wanting to endure a worried, sleepless night I rang the GP practice and was told to bring Anna down straight away to check her breathing. Anna was in such discomfort she had to be admitted that evening to the Children's Assessment Unit at the Leicester Royal Infirmary. This led to a chest x-ray being done to check the status of the original air bubble that had developed following surgery. It was minimal, but all the doctors wanted to keep her in overnight to monitor her breathing and pain levels. Neither of us wanted to spend another night in hospital despite everyone being so friendly and supportive, but it couldn't be helped.

In the end, Anna didn't need any specific treatment but it was felt that she would benefit from being prescribed more codeine (which coincidentally had run out the night before she started to experience the rib pain) to help manage the pain better. We were very pleased that that was all that was required and wished we'd been prescribed more than five days' worth on discharge from hospital in Nottingham.

Both of us were very glad to be heading for home and were relieved when Andy came to pick us up. I had had very little sleep during the night owing to the children's ward playing music, albeit quietly, throughout the night, possibly to help children sleep, but I was very aware of it and even listened to it while getting more and more frustrated that it was playing at all!

By Thursday evening we were back to our usual routines and couldn't believe that nearly two full weeks had passed since surgery.

FIFTEEN

The first shower

By Saturday morning Anna was desperate to wash her hair, so armed with numerous pillows to kneel on and plenty of towels around her to ensure her wound couldn't possibly get wet, we worked together and successfully managed to achieve a reasonable hair wash. We still couldn't remove all the remaining glue from the areas where the electrodes had been stuck to her scalp, but the majority had finally gone.

What a difference having clean hair made. Anna felt far more cheerful, looked much more like her old self and decided she would definitely be up to seeing friends who had been texting her frequently to see when they could visit.

Her first visitor was her good friend, Eve, who came round in the afternoon with a beautiful bouquet of flowers and her favourite chocolates to enjoy. Although Anna was exhausted after only forty-five minutes or so, the visit had boosted her feelings of well-being and of being connected to her 'normal' world again. It was a good step forward.

On Sunday, another close friend, Natalie, visited, with delicious homemade cakes and plenty of news about school and friends. Just to hear laughter coming from the lounge rather than the bell jingling was wonderful and meant I could relax, knowing that Anna was also relaxed and happy.

Having such supportive friends was a real boost to

Anna's recovery because she was still too weak to walk anywhere outside and car journeys were still best avoided or kept very short. At the weekend Andrew and I had thought it would be good to get out in the fresh air and had taken her on a ten-minute journey to a local garden centre so she could eat delicious chocolate ice cream in different surroundings from home. However, it had transpired that the car journey made Anna feel sick, despite being padded by two pillows and a cushion, and even the twenty-yard walk to the entrance had been totally exhausting. Then, sitting in the chair in the café was very uncomfortable as we hadn't brought any pillows to support her back, and after a few mouthfuls of ice cream Anna was unable to eat any more.

We realised that it was simply too early to plan such a trip and we subsequently decided to be guided by Anna a little more and wait for her to suggest when she was ready for an outing. She assured us that we were doing plenty for her and didn't need to plan outings on her behalf.

That evening I changed the wound dressing, aware that the hospital discharge notes recommended that the wound and how it was healing should be checked after two weeks.

I hadn't received an appointment from the practice nurse so decided to photo the scar and email it to our scoliosis nurse at the Queens Medical Centre. Thank goodness for modern technology. To me the scar still looked quite red and matted and I didn't know if this was normal or not. At any rate we still didn't think it looked healed enough to have a shower even though we knew Emma, Matt's friend, had had a shower less than a week after surgery. We both felt that sink washes should be continued for a few more days.

Monday morning heralded the start of a week when

Anna was due to sit a Science GCSE module that Friday. I went to her school and collected plenty of reading material for her to revise from; all the staff were so helpful and we were told the invigilator from school would arrive on Friday at 9am and, although it was due to last 45 minutes, Anna would be given some extra time so that she could lie down or rest after 20 minutes.

We also had a visit from one of the Hospital Outreach teachers, Peter, who gave Anna an hour of English tuition, which was brilliant, particularly as she had an English GCSE module in June. After the hour, which Anna managed to sit and concentrate through fairly well, she felt reassured that she hadn't fallen too far behind with her studies and hopefully would be up to the standard required when the exam date arrived.

On Tuesday morning we decided, after discussion with the scoliosis nurse, that Anna should have a shower to hopefully wash off the steri-strips. If they didn't wash off, our scoliosis nurse felt they should be taken off by the practice nurse. It was a brilliant decision. Anna finally felt totally clean and refreshed, giving her renewed energy to face the day. I then very carefully and slowly peeled off the thirty steri-strips, revealing an incredibly thin, neat scar.

It all looked great apart from right at the bottom of the scar, which looked as though it hadn't fully healed over. Part of a stitch looked visible so I decided to keep a close eye on it over the next few days. The last thing Anna needed was an infection, but at the same time I didn't want to rush her onto more antibiotics (she was given a big dose during the operation) without good reason. It didn't look infected and I hoped by keeping it clean and dry it would settle down.

It was another step in the right direction although Anna was then exhausted and needed a well-earned lie-down before she had enough energy to think about doing some revision for the science exam on Friday.

After an hour of revision she was wiped out; it made me consider whether or not she would be well enough for full-time school in another four weeks — students are allowed back after scoliosis surgery after only six weeks if they're ready. Her school had said she could return part-time if necessary and would be very flexible. Anna could dictate what she felt ready for and when, which helped her feel in control of the situation.

Friday morning dawned, which marked the three-week milestone and a science exam to be taken at home. The invigilator sent from school was a lovely lady, about to retire that summer, who put Anna at ease immediately. Anna had been worried that she wouldn't be strong enough to sit the exam but in the event only needed one rest break to lie down and take some pain relief before completing the paper.

It had been challenging, considering that she hadn't been at school to prepare, but she felt she had done her best and I was extremely proud of her positive attitude and upbeat outlook under quite difficult circumstances. We felt immensely grateful to Cheryl, a wonderful tutor, who had also given Anna some help and guidance during the week.

Three of Anna's friends came round after school, armed with chocolate, magazines and lots of chat. Even though Anna could only manage about an hour of conversation it cheered her up tremendously to know that her friends were all thinking about her; they probably didn't realise what a positive impact all of their visits made.

After they had all gone we had a short walk to the bottom of the garden and back to see how much stamina for walking she had built up. The short stroll was enough, and she didn't feel able to sit outside but was keen to get back to the refuge of the settee, which was proving comfortable for both sitting and lying, aided by various cushions and pillows.

She was still conscientiously doing all the exercises set by the physiotherapists twice a day and could now put on and pull up leggings without help. She found that her overall mobility was better; she could walk a little faster from room to room and up and down the stairs, but didn't have enough energy to go for a walk outside longer than twenty yards or so. Another week and maybe that goal of walking further will have been achieved. I was hoping the weather would improve so that walking outside would seem more enticing. Having a wind gusting in your face is not conducive to a lovely walk and the forecast for half-term was unfortunately fairly bleak!

SIXTEEN

Daily routines

Saturday was the first day into the fourth week and meant another shower, another dressing change and another scrutiny of the scar. Unfortunately, the base of the scar seemed unchanged, which was positive in that it still seemed uninfected, but frustrating that it hadn't healed over completely. My monitoring would have to continue to Tuesday, which was the deadline I had set myself before seeking advice from the practice nurse.

Anna found that she could now cough properly, so her ribs were obviously healing, which was fantastic news. She still found that her shoulder pain from the costoplasty continued but her back now only felt stiff and wasn't particularly painful unless she unwittingly moved too quickly. We were both hoping that in only a few more days she would be able to manage without the codeine tablets, which provided the strongest pain relief.

Sunday passed uneventfully. Anna was now an expert on all her favourite serials and shows. She had a great number of DVD viewings under her belt as well and I'm sure would have been able to put film critics to shame with her newly-acquired knowledge.

She found reading books too tiring on her arms and shoulders and couldn't find a comfortable way of holding them, but maybe that was an excuse not to start reading all the novels I had selected for her from the library. They were all stacked in the dining room, moving only when the table needed laying or when I thought a different resting place might make them more enticing! I didn't really appreciate how tiring Anna found it just concentrating on a book, so television continued to provide the best entertainment.

Bank Holiday Monday dawned with grey skies and little appeal for a walk, but passed easily in the house with Anna's usual routine of washing, lying down, doing her exercises, walking round the house, sitting and lying down again. This pattern was repeated throughout the day, but at least she had the distraction of us all talking to her and involving her in decisions and topics of conversation.

Even though she found it more comfortable sitting on the settee than anywhere else downstairs, we encouraged her to sit with us at the dining-room table for family meals, her back supported by a pillow, because it provided a diversion from the monotony of her daily routine and kept her involved with family life. I was thankful that she had such a sunny disposition and didn't seem outwardly depressed by her repetitive schedule and lack of excitement and variety.

It would have been very easy for her to sink into dark moods, particularly during this half-term week when all her friends had plans for shopping trips to Nottingham and Birmingham, cinema visits and meals out to celebrate birthdays. However, Anna seemed to share in their happiness while being aware that she just had to be patient and recover at home. I was so proud of her and really believed that she had a tremendous inner core of strength.

She was certainly rising to her challenge and taking all the steps, both forwards and at times backwards, in her stride, and all of it with an amazing strength and sense of humour.

On Thursday Anna was invited to spend an hour at a friend's house, which made a welcome break from the same four walls which were starting to get a little claustrophobic for her. Thank goodness for the warm June weather which now allowed Anna to spend some time sitting in the garden.

In the afternoon she tentatively asked if she could have a second ear piercing while off school. She had definitely earned a treat, particularly as Matt and Rachel had been able to meet up with friends during the week and do various fun activities which Anna couldn't be part of, so I readily agreed. Anna wanted it to be a surprise for the rest of the family so the appointment duly booked for the following week was kept a secret. We booked in person so Anna could choose the style of earring she wanted (a blue sapphire-effect stud); this marked her first visit into Oadby since the operation.

Other firsts this week included being able to dress completely independently apart from putting shoes on, sitting without a break for over an hour, and sleeping for more than eight hours at night without needing any pain relief. She also needed fewer pain killers in the day, and if she hadn't had the costoplasty would probably have been off them altogether. Her shoulder still felt stiff and quite sore, but her back was just stiff. The physiotherapy exercises were really helping and she conscientiously did them once a day, and if she remembered, twice.

Her scar continued to heal well and by this time looked like a neat red pen line down her back. The very end of the base of the scar had still not fully healed over so I still had to change the dressing carefully after showers to keep it clean and dry.

SEVENTEEN

Home tuition

This week brought serious revision and exam preparation in Science and English in readiness for the GCSE exam modules the following week, which Anna would be able to take at home with an invigilator from Beauchamp College as before. Fortunately, the hospital school had been able to offer three one-hour sessions with English teachers on Monday, Wednesday and Friday, which provided a good structure for Anna to work round. Her English teacher had also already provided us with texts and past papers, which were very helpful.

Matt had his last AS paper on the Monday, which heralded a couple of weeks off school for him before A2 study commenced. This made Anna feel less isolated, although Rachel felt slightly frustrated that she had to attend school every day while, in her eyes, Matt and Anna were lazing around the house. I reminded her that they were both revising hard for upcoming exams and she would have the same privilege in years to come!

I emailed our scoliosis nurse in Nottingham to see whether Anna could have her six-week follow-up appointment with the consultant while off school. I was also hoping that Matt could have his follow-up appointment at the same time in order to avoid making two separate trips to the x-ray department. He had remained free from back pain and displayed no obvious abnormalities, so I really hoped that there would be no change at all to the Cobb angle, and in fact hoped that his back might have straightened, as he had grown slightly.

This week also marked my return to work, although being part-time meant that Anna wasn't on her own all day and Andy could pop back at lunch times when I was unable to. My work colleagues had sent two beautiful cards with lovely messages inside, which was a real boost to receive. Just knowing that people were thinking of us and praying for Anna's continued recovery helped us all feel positive and cheerful. In fact when I got to school I thought someone had left raffle prizes in my room as I was greeted with a beautiful bouquet of gorgeous flowers and a bag of chocolates, biscuits and wine. I was so surprised and overwhelmed when I learnt that they were for me, Anna and the whole family to enjoy. I really felt extremely lucky to be working in such a supportive school with incredibly caring and wonderful people.

Anna couldn't believe her eyes either and as she was the first person I saw on my return home (Matt was with friends and Rachel at athletics club) we decided that the pralines could be kept as our secret, and after eating several varieties each, hid them in Anna's bedroom!

Anna had had a difficult week suffering with leg pains and aching muscles. Andy and I wondered whether she was still in 'poorly patient' mode and now needed to significantly reduce the amount of TV she was watching and try to build up her stamina and strength. For three consecutive nights she had been unable to sleep right through and I had had to massage her legs for half hour periods to try and relieve the pains and aches.

Our doctor felt that these were partly due to reduced use and partly because her whole body had been realigned since surgery and the muscles in her legs had to readjust. She decided to refer Anna for some physiotherapy to help build up her leg muscles, so we hoped an appointment would be sent fairly quickly, particularly as we learnt that the follow-up appointment with the consultant would not be six weeks post-op but three months, so we were not due an outpatient appointment until August. However, this did mean that Matt could be sent an appointment at the same time as a year had almost passed since his first x-ray and it would certainly be easier only making one trip. Matt and Anna were also quite keen to see each other's x-rays!

Neither Emma nor Ruth had suffered with these leg pains, and all the articles and reports I had read about other children post-surgery seemed to indicate that they were back at school easily after six weeks and there were no problems with mobility, pain or stiffness. So, on Thursday I made the decision to take down all the get-well cards which had decorated the entire lounge for nearly five weeks, and give them to her to keep as a reminder (she loves cards), as, after a chat, we agreed that they could be contributing to her mental attitude of being a 'patient', whereas now she had to start believing she was well and concentrate on building her strength up. She was on far fewer painkillers now, and although her ribs were still sensitive when she showered, her back was essentially just stiff and not painful.

The stitch at the base of her scar had frustratingly still not disappeared so had not allowed the scar in that area to fully heal over. This meant that we still needed to continue dressing the scar after Anna had a shower to prevent the scar being knocked. I really didn't want Anna to get an infection in the scar at this late stage and I wasn't taking any chances! I rang the practice nurse to get her opinion on the scar and how it was healing. She thought it sounded as though there was a stitch protruding slightly but in time it should dissolve and heal well.

Anna had also started to feel quite disheartened with her progress so it was fortunate that I could take her into Oadby to get the second ear piercing we had booked. This involved a short walk, which was good physiotherapy and a mental boost, because she arrived home very happy and excited at the prospect of showing all her friends the new gem.

Friday dawned and marked five weeks since the operation. She now had only one more week before she was officially allowed back to school. We both felt that she had quite a way to go if she was going to cope with a full day, so resolved that the following week would involve an increased effort to develop her mobility and stamina. She was due to have her final GCSE exams for that term on the Wednesday and Friday, so would also have to revise as hard as she could.

EIGHTEEN

Leg pains

Saturday morning came and we were now into the sixth week of recovery. Every week seemed like a mini milestone, but this one seemed especially important because of the expectation that Anna would be going back to school the following Monday.

Over the weekend Anna continued to have terrible aching pains in her legs, which improved slightly if she held a heat bag or hot water bottle over them, but were particularly bad at night time, and she was finding it difficult to get a good night's sleep. The feeling of being breathless and struggling to get enough air had also returned. We didn't know of anyone else who had had these symptoms following surgery so decided to visit our GP once more, for reassurance and advice.

Our GP felt that Anna could be anaemic because she was so pale, breathless and generally lacking the energy levels expected, although she reminded us not to underestimate how invasive the surgery had been and that everyone is different in the rate of progress made. For Anna it was likely to be longer anyway because of the costoplasty procedure she had to have in order to try and reduce the rib hump. She decided a blood test would help make a diagnosis and fortunately the practice nurse had a space that day which meant we should know the results by the end of the week.

I felt slightly awful that I had been trying to jolly Anna

along, persuading her that she needed to increase her stamina by doing more; I never thought about the possibility of her now being anaemic. She had needed a blood transfusion during surgery because of the amount of blood loss, but I had assumed that this would have returned her iron levels to normal, and she hadn't had any blood tests since the operation. Until we got the results I decided to cook a variety of iron-rich meals, washed down by orange juice, because I knew that vitamin C helped the body absorb iron more easily. Fortunately, one of Anna's favourite meals is spaghetti bolognaise and by chance she had enjoyed roast lamb and homemade beef burgers over the weekend!

We had also received an appointment with a physiotherapist who could hopefully prescribe more exercises to build up her strength and mobility.

By Thursday, the blood test results were back and proved negative for any deficiencies, although Anna was advised to eat plenty of iron-rich foods. However, since the Monday appointment, I had bought multivitamin and iron tablets which Anna had been taking daily, and the improvement even after two days was incredible; she had more energy, wanted to try walking outside further (she was now up to half-an-hour bursts) and even felt she might be up to going to the cinema with a friend at the weekend.

Needless to say, despite the blood test results, Anna was keen to keep taking the daily tablet until the bottle ran out. Finally, I thought she was well and truly on the way to being back to normal. She has now said she even feels glad to have had the operation because of how much straighter her back feels. She has been trying to reassure Matt that it would be definitely worth it if he needed the same procedure. We should know whether or not that would be necessary following his second x-ray, which was due in August.

Friday marked the six-week milestone and Anna's final GCSE exam that term. Her final science exam was again completed at home with an invigilator from her school in attendance. She felt positive about her performance and relieved that she could now concentrate on completing all the coursework she had missed without any time pressures, and really focus on getting strong and well. She hoped to go back to school in a couple of weeks for the remainder of the summer term, and expected to be fully fit by September and the new academic year.

NINETEEN

Physiotherapy helps

This week has been like a new chapter in Anna's life because her energy levels have really started to increase, and for four days she has managed to last all day without needing to lie down at all.

She needs only occasional pain relief for her shoulder pain, which is probably due to the costoplasty rather than the spinal re-positioning, and is able to sleep normally again without the leg pains which have been plaguing her. I still help her put on her fluorescent-pink leg warmers at night because this does seem to help, but she hasn't used any heat bags for well over a week.

Although she is not back at school yet she is managing a daily walk of 30-40 minutes and is able to give her attention to course-work projects for school during the day. She still tires easily and doesn't feel that she would have the stamina to sustain a full or even half day at school. This is because it is such a large college and involves a fair amount of walking as well as a lot of sitting in chairs that would not necessarily compare favourably to our leather settee!

Our liaison staff member at school has been brilliant and could arrange special seating for Anna and a bed in the medical room for her to rest on at any point in the school day if she wished, but Anna is really keen to go back to school without needing any special arrangements and is determined this week to really build up her strength and stamina so that the goal of starting school the following week becomes a reality.

On Friday we saw the consultant, who was very pleased with Anna's progress, particularly as she is recovering from *two* surgical procedures. He stressed that every patient's recovery time was individual and that Anna must not compare herself to others. Of course he didn't realise that this was, in fact, just what Anna had done by googling other patients' stories in Britain and abroad, and had recently discovered one American girl who had been photographed by her family walking out of hospital after only four days, waving and even carrying a small rucksack. This was in contrast to Anna who was discharged after a week and left in a wheelchair supported by pillows. On arriving home she had walked extremely slowly and stiffly into the house watched by her brother and sister who were open-mouthed in horror (both of course fervently hoping that they would not have inherited scoliosis and have to undergo surgery too). On seeing their faces she did try to smile bravely and stressed that the discomfort was caused by the costoplasty and not her back!

We did mention that the base of the scar seemed to have a bit of stitching poking out, so our consultant gently rubbed this and the stitch just fell away, which meant we could finally dispel with any dressings after showering; if only we had had the confidence to rub it gently ourselves!

Anna had a chest x-ray just to check the lungs were fully expanding because Anna still felt she needed to inhale very deeply at times to get enough air. Fortunately this revealed that her lungs were definitely working well and the air bubble had now been completely absorbed.

On the Friday afternoon we then saw the most fantastic physiotherapist, Theresa, who assessed Anna and prescribed exercises to help her correct a slight rotation of her pelvis as she walked, which could be contributing to the leg pains. She also examined Anna's back. She admired the very neat scar that had already become a pale pink line and was so thin and neat it was hard to imagine the invasive surgery that had caused it. She commented on the rib hump that was still noticeable on one side, although hugely better than it had been, and to most people's eyes probably not noticeable at all. She then went on to say, and this was the most fantastic moment (second only to my feelings of joy when I was told that Anna's surgery had been very successful and she was in recovery), that exercises could eliminate the rib hump completely. Anna was standing with her back facing me and I watched as Theresa gently rotated her shoulder back and expertly eased her shoulder into the correct position.

"Oh my goodness, Anna," I couldn't help exclaiming, "your rib hump has just completely disappeared and your back looks totally normal!"

What a terrific moment and one I could capture on film as, fortunately, I had my camera with me. The 'before' and 'after' photos would probably not have been especially impressive to an onlooker, but to us the 'after' photo was a wonderful goal she could now strive towards, and I felt so euphoric that her back would look symmetrical at last. Her words of only a few weeks ago floated into my mind. 'You know, when I sit back, my hump still touches the back of the settee first'. She had stated this sadly but matter-of-factly because it was so much better than before surgery, but now we learned that this could be corrected too. The muscles had been in an incorrect position for so long that they didn't move into the correct position post-surgery and needed very specific exercises to ensure they re-learned the correct position to go with Anna's new body shape.

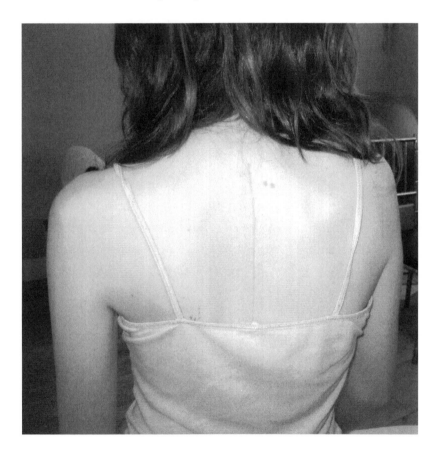

Physiotherapy helped reduce the hump completely

We went home feeling elated, and that evening Anna was well enough to take part in her dance class's 'showcase' evening for parents. It was only an hour long and Anna only had a small acting part, but when she walked confidently onto the stage I felt my heart swell with pride and I wanted to turn round and shout to everyone, "Look! Anna had major surgery seven weeks ago and here she is on stage. She's my amazing daughter!" She spoke her part clearly and fluently and I know I applauded the loudest! This was a real turning point and occasionally I even began to forget that Anna wasn't back to full health!

Every day now held new achievements, such as the first swim. She had been a very strong, stylish swimmer as a much younger girl, and swimming now proved to be a fantastic feeling for Anna because her back was fully supported by the water and she found she could move quite easily, so although she initially found it a very strange sensation, she was able to swim eight lengths. Nonetheless she got breathless quite easily and found it much easier on her back than her front because her back seemed heavy, as though it was pushing her down in the water.

It was so good to be able to do a normal physical activity again, and when we went a second time, only a few days later, Anna found it easier still. This time Rachel came as well and it was good to see both girls swimming the length of the pool together, chatting as they went.

On our second visit Theresa was very pleased with Anna's progress and she gave her new exercises to complete twice a day. I also made an appointment for Matt because Theresa believed that exercises to build up his core strength could prevent his curvature from progressing, and might even decrease it. We were certainly willing to try, and even Matt, who is often quite sceptical about such things, was willing to give physiotherapy a go, particularly as he had a second x-ray and appointment with the consultant scheduled for August.

During the week, Rachel attended her school's sports day and as the school is only round the corner from our house Anna was able to go and support her as Andrew and I unfortunately had work commitments. Anna took photos at every event and even chatted to Rachel as she followed her round the different challenges. Several parents later spoke to me about how impressed they were with Anna's mobility and confided that they would have never guessed she was recovering from such major surgery. It was another positive step forward and I know Anna felt pleased that she was making such good progress.

TWENTY

Back at school

A bright, sunny Monday morning in July heralded Anna's first day back at school since May 5th. She was up bright and early but rather nervous about going back to a routine she had not been part of for two months.

Seeing her straighten her hair looking just like her old self was a positive sight and made me very thankful that life was finally returning to normal. She set off in Andrew's car (we had agreed to take her to and from school to minimise the amount of walking she needed to do to help keep her energy levels as high as possible) with a smile on her face as if to say 'What is all the fuss about?' I half-expected a phone call from her or school during the day but it passed uneventfully and when I saw her outside Beauchamp College later that afternoon she looked well and happy. "How was your day?" was answered with a matter-of-fact "Fine, thanks". I needn't have worried!

She went from strength to strength as the week progressed and seemed to fit straight back into work and school life without any difficulties. She even felt able to walk home by herself on the Friday, picking Rachel up on the way. So from being at home full time she had progressed to completing a week of full-time school. There were no half-measures! She didn't even need pain relief to help her through the day and now only needed tablets at night. She even let slip to Andrew and me that she had been visiting the local supermarket during lunchtime (which many of the students did) but insisted it was only a 'tiny walk'. We both agreed that if that was the case she should be more than able to walk to and from school next week and wouldn't need our taxi service!

On Saturday and Sunday she and Rachel took part in the 'Lemon Jelly Dance Show' at Uppingham Theatre. This involved practising during the two days and performing both evenings. Andy and I were filled with pride at both girls' performances on the Sunday evening, but when Anna came on stage confidently and purposefully it made all the heartache and anxiety of the last two months fade away. What an incredible achievement for her.

It had been an amazing week of positive steps and heart-warming moments. It is still early days and overall progress will only be measured by us when a full year has elapsed after the operation, but at least the days are now filled with delight at what Anna can do, rather than what she still can't do.

While they were practising for the show I went shopping and saw a little vintage house I knew she would like, and when I read the little plaque on the door knew I had to buy it for her. It read:

If you can walk
you can dance
If you can talk
you can sing

As Anna was due to resume her singing lessons the following week, it fitted her situation exactly. I knew she would treasure the sentiments and use them to give her continued strength and determination as she developed the skills needed to be a performer on the stage, and help her follow her dream.

The last week of school went well and on the last day we recalled how it had been exactly a year to the day when she had had the MRI scan before we travelled to Malta. It was wonderful to have all those memories behind us as we looked forward to travelling to Turkey for a fortnight's relaxing in the sun.

The holiday abroad was as relaxing and enjoyable as we had imagined and Anna took part in everything, from swimming in the pool to snorkelling in the sea. She even managed an unplanned short jog to the sea on Turtle Beach where the sand was so hot it burnt your feet if you didn't move quickly!

She only took pain relief a couple of times throughout the holiday, and really, we almost forgot she had had the operation, despite it being only nine weeks earlier. She was very careful to keep her scar well covered (the scoliosis nurse had emphasised that if the scar gets burnt it will never fade fully) so wore T-shirts while swimming in the pool. It was healing so well and had already faded to a pale pink line which was long but very neat.

We came home the day after the twelve-week milestone feeling very refreshed, and when I saw the holiday photos I couldn't believe how well and healthy Anna looked in her bikini. Last year, when I was filled with so many anxieties, seemed like a lifetime ago, so watching Anna laughing and joking with Rachel in the pool filled me with amazement and relief. We were both quite looking forward to the three-month follow-up appointment the following week to see how straight her spine had become.

On holiday in Turkey, nine weeks after surgery

TWENTY-ONE

X-ray results

Both Anna and Matthew had an appointment with our consultant on Monday, August 1st for follow-up x-rays, and after having these taken, both waited patiently to be called in to see him.

We were surprised to see one of Anna's friend's sister in the waiting room with her mum, both looking anxious and equally surprised to see us! She had just been diagnosed with idiopathic scoliosis and, like us a year ago, didn't really know anything about the condition and also didn't know anyone who had it.

We reassured her, answered some questions and even managed to raise a smile when we said that once Anna had been diagnosed we found that nearly everyone we knew had a friend, or knew a relative, or had experience of scoliosis. We were even able to tell them about a Turkish man, Vedat, who we hired a boat from while on holiday in July, who had a sister-in-law with the condition and who had been operated on in Turkey years ago.

The following week we found out that Anna's orthodontist's nephew had had the operation the previous year and lots of our friends could now tell us of someone they knew with the condition. Yet before Anna was diagnosed, not only had I not even heard of it, I didn't know or even know of, a single person with scoliosis. It felt unbelievable how things changed. Maybe conditions only become known when you are actively searching for them. It certainly caused Anna and me to have a laugh about it because our lack of knowledge was one of the key reasons that I started to write my book.

Anna was first to receive feedback and our consultant was pleased to report that she was making excellent progress and her back was healing well. Her spine looked pretty straight to us on the x-ray but Anna was disappointed to learn that the curve had now stabilised at 27 degrees; this was the straightest it would be but shouldn't now get any worse. However, the side profile of her spine was excellent and this was the position the consultant was more concerned about.

I tried to reassure Anna on the way home that twenty-seven was just a number and before we had the appointment we were both very pleased with how her back looked. And I encouraged her that if she continued doing all the physiotherapy exercises, the slight remnant of her hump would continue to decrease.

Overall it was positive news and we hoped there wouldn't be any changes at the next appointment which was due to be three months later, so at the six-month milestone.

Matthew was slightly apprehensive as we waited for his x-ray result, but fortunately this revealed that his curve had not altered significantly since the previous October so he could now be discharged from the department. This was good news and Matthew was heartily relieved that he wouldn't need the operation.

At the next physiotherapy appointment Theresa was very pleased with Anna's progress and concluded that she wouldn't need another appointment for a couple of months, but should continue with the on-going exercises to help strengthen her legs and reduce the hump on her back, which was already insignificant to a casual observer. Only we knew that it wasn't yet completely flat, although the 'winging' of the shoulder blade was much less than before we went on holiday.

The holidays progressed and on the 18th August Anna set off with a friend to discover how well she had done in the two GCSE exams she had taken early—English Language and one of the Double Science GCSEs which is completed after one year. Anna had had to sit several exams at home, and combined with the knowledge that she had missed almost two months of school, made her unsure of what grades to expect. I was just hoping that she had managed to pass them both, so when I heard the door open and saw a very happy face appear round the door, I felt quite excited.

We waited expectantly.

"I got an A for English Language and a B for Science!" she announced delightedly. Another step in the right direction that meant Anna could now look forward to her final GCSE year knowing that she wouldn't need any days off and could concentrate on working hard. The only exam that would still be a little uncertain was her Dance GCSE because her flexibility was still very reduced and she still got back pain if she overdid walking, standing for too long etc, so we weren't sure how dancing energetically would affect her. Thankfully her teacher had already said that she could leave the practical exams until near the end of the year, probably May, and also emphasised to Anna that the letter from our GP outlining her difficulties would be sent with all her written and practical work.

I felt anyway that a lot of the back pain and stiffness she had now was most likely due to her doing more, and the muscles around her spine being used more, and of course they had to adapt to being in a different position now that her spine was straight. The positive fact was that she now rarely took any pain relief despite getting occasional backache. All her friends now perceived her as being 'back to normal', which sometimes made her feel a little frustrated because she still couldn't run or take part in any contact sports. She also couldn't ride on roller coasters yet so wasn't able to join her friends on a trip to Alton Towers. 'A small price to pay for long-term health', I reminded her, and she agreed. She has always been pretty pragmatic about what she could and couldn't do because of her back, and was good at being positive and looking to the future and the successes she was going to achieve. I inwardly continued to admire her strength.

TWENTY-TWO:

Can and can't dos

September brought the start of the new academic year. Anna is now able to walk to and from school easily. Backaches are infrequent and she can participate in PE apart from tennis this first term; hitting with a racket is fine if she could only remain stationary, but of course tennis involves running quickly to and from different parts of the court, and stretching arms, legs and back at different times. This proved too painful when she tentatively had a try.

She has to go to the school gym during the tennis sessions, where she can cycle on the exercise bikes. She would rather help pick up the balls in tennis for friends, or at least be part of the whole group doing some sort of activity, but rules are rules and she is not allowed to be a bystander so has had to accept solitary time in the gym. A bit harsh, she feels, but at least the cycling will help to build up her muscle strength and stamina, which is a positive thing.

Anna feels that her back is now totally different to the back she had before surgery and has realised that she just has to accept that it feels different and that in time this will become her 'normal' back. She is already feeling that this is the case, and although the days in hospital now seem a lifetime away, I keep reminding her that it was only four months ago and so, in the context of the year of recovery, she is still less than half way. It is still early days and she is right to listen to her body and be aware of her limitations, while continuing with daily walking and physiotherapy exercises—although there are odd days when she and I both completely forget!

Anna has just glanced over my shoulder to check I am writing accurately and including all the positives and negatives about what she can and can't do at this point. She offered to jot down all the important points she's aware of. This list is the result:

- Bending down is difficult because I have to keep my back straight.

- Heavy things are still quite hard to pick up eg a chair.

- Slow running feels very weird and uncomfortable and after a while, painful.

- I experience a lot of pain and stiffness in my hump when I sit down for a long time.

- I still have to get into bed on my side.

- I have a lot more movement than just after the operation.

- I have jerked my body by accident a few times, which hurts.

- When I do new movements I can feel the rods and pins moving around, which feels really weird.

- My ribs near the top can feel uncomfortable when stretching.

- I can't do many sports, which is very frustrating.

- I find it a bit easier to put tights on, and tight trousers, but it still hurts to bend over for those tasks.

- My left thigh has still not got normal sensation and if I bang it, it really hurts, much more than the other side which feels normal.

- It's very hard to wash my feet with soap in the shower.

- I can't bend down to tie up shoes because my back feels too heavy and it is too uncomfortable; I bend my knee and bring my foot closer to me!

- I have not yet jumped at all because I am too worried that it might damage my back.

Anna gave me this list matter-of-factly and is now watching a television show without further thought, but it has made me think how guilty I am of almost forgetting what she has been through and still how far she has to go to be 'normal' in her eyes. She was such an athletic, sporty girl before, and a fantastic runner, and I do feel for her. I hope so much that she will be able to run fast and competitively again and play tennis in the future and do all the sports and hobbies she wants. I feel a huge sense of pride that she carries on in such a positive manner; she never ever moans about her pains or restrictions or lets herself get frustrated or upset by what she can't do. We continually focus on what she can do and I think that has helped us all enormously.

She is able to take delight in other people's achievements without letting herself get down. For example, this second weekend in September I played in a club tennis tournament and had to play much more than my usual once a week, and in fact ended up reaching the handicap singles final. Although I lost this final match I was to receive a small prize and Anna said she would like to come and watch the presentation. So all three children (Andrew was playing golf!) came down to the club with me and watched the final games being played before the prizes were given out. Anna was pleased and supportive and never once mentioned how much she herself misses sports, although I know she must do. I'm continually filled with pride on how she has adapted to her situation with such a positive outlook and complete lack of self-pity.

We had a chat a few days later about possible options for 'A' level and Anna felt that she couldn't do PE because she wouldn't be able to use a trampoline, and that is one of the focus sports. She feels, without any undertones of feeling sorry for herself, that she probably won't be able to dance either. However, I think we should just wait and see until the day she gets her GCSE results. Recovery has been set at a year, and by then I'm hoping she will be able to resume many of her activities properly and without discomfort.

Shortly after that chat Anna discovered that she had achieved 100% for the first module of her Drama GCSE; this was the highest mark in the whole year and we were all absolutely delighted for her and the tremendous boost this gave to her self-esteem and confidence. "An A* student", I proclaimed, and she allowed herself a smile. It prompted another discussion about possible future jobs, and for the first time Anna talked about acting and drama as a career rather than dancing. She admitted to having thought long and hard about dancing, but ultimately recognised in her heart of hearts that dancing in the West End is such a coveted job and so highly competitive that now she is less flexible she probably wouldn't get selected.

But rather than dwell on that disappointment she went on, in the next breath, to tell me that her new dream is of becoming a famous actress and that she would put all her energies into trying to achieve that goal.

She is proving to be tremendously resilient and I'm continually proud of the way she deals with her various dilemmas in such a down-to earth way. She is continuing to build up her stamina through exercise and this should be consolidated when we visit Center Parcs in half-term. I'm hoping she will even be able to go down some of the slides and maybe join in with gentle badminton.

We will continue to focus on all the activities she can do, and hopefully enjoy a relaxing week together.

TWENTY-THREE

Proper exercise

At the beginning of the month Anna's school held an Open Morning to give students an opportunity to decide possible 'A' level options for the following year.

We spoke to many of the different subject teachers, who helped Anna decide that her choices at A2 level would be Drama, English Literature and Psychology. After discussion with her dance teacher (who has always been so supportive and accommodating towards Anna) she decided that she could do dancing up to AS level but drop this after one year. She seemed happy and settled with her decision although changes can be made right up until the day of the GCSE results next August. She then focused on her studies for the next six weeks.

Half-term came around quickly and on a crisp autumn morning we departed for a break near the Lake District. The long drive up to Center Parcs in Cumbria was made in glorious autumn sunshine, and all our spirits were high when we finally reached our villa. Andrew parked the car after unloading all our bikes and we were ready for a relaxing five-day break.

Anna was looking forward to experimenting on her bike; she hadn't attempted cycling since her operation and we were all hoping she would manage successfully. Needless to say she was completely fine. Admittedly there were a few small hills to negotiate and both she and Rachel found it easier to walk up those, but mostly she cycled well.

She felt it was the first time she had really had to push herself physically since surgery and she told me several times that she was very unfit now! However, she persevered, and by the end of the break was finding it increasingly easier and she enjoyed being out in open. The trees surrounding the villas towered over us and provided a home to many different birds and animals. We frequently had a grouse or squirrel outside our window and were lucky enough to see the rare red squirrels; Andrew even managed to get a close up photo for the album. It was beautiful countryside and we were fortunate to have good weather so that we could fully appreciate it.

As predicted, Anna didn't dare risk any of the slides in the swimming pools and splash areas because the small flumes jolted even *my* back and I didn't want a few minutes of fun to cause long-term damage to the pins or rods in hers. She was happy to swim in the main pool, lazy river and spa pools, so could relax and enjoy the water with the rest of us without feeling that she was missing out.

We didn't try ten pin bowling because Anna thought the balls would be too heavy, but she did have a tentative go at badminton which before her operation she really enjoyed. She hadn't got a full range of movements and couldn't run around the court, but nonetheless she managed to keep rallies going quite successfully and won many good points. It was great fun, particularly as we could all join in.

We all enjoyed a large quantity of calorie-laden hot drinks and cookies (particularly the chocolate chunk cookies) throughout our stay, but felt virtuous as were doing so much exercise every day!

The eating of sweet things continued when we visited Blackpool on our journey back to Leicester. The freshly made doughnuts on the sea front tasted absolutely delicious . . . and Mr Whippy ice creams of course . . . and a small candy floss!

We arrived home feeling relaxed, refreshed and pleased that Anna had been able to join in with most activities. However, several days after being back at school, Anna told me that her back now felt stiffer than before and she was also getting shooting pains up her back. We wondered whether, because she was becoming more mobile, her muscles were perhaps being stretched more.

She decided that she wouldn't do any more PE at school (she had occasionally been joining in with gentle tennis) in case she had done too much at Center Parcs and had perhaps done some damage. I agreed that maybe she should just listen to her body and only do as much as she felt able to on any particular day.

Her next x-ray (the six-month follow-up) and appointment with our consultant was due on November 7th and we were hoping for good news, that everything was progressing well.

TWENTY-FOUR

Six-month milestone

It didn't seem as if six months had passed since surgery as we set off to the hospital on November 7th, the distant memory of all the severe discomfort being well and truly behind us. We now felt quite excited and optimistic as we waited to be called in to see our consultant after already having had the x-rays taken.

The now familiar sight of his computer screen flashed up with the most recent image and, thank goodness, this time there were no shocks or surprises in store for us.

Anna's curve still measured 26 degrees (it had been 27 degrees in August so only a negligible difference today), so basically it had not moved and the pins were now very stable and secure in her back. Although a curve of 26 degrees sounds moderately severe to most people (including me before Anna and Matt had been diagnosed) it is actually quite minimal in terms of movement and overall appearance, so we were actually very happy that no further movement had occurred and Anna's back was now essentially stable.

She was given the go-ahead to play tennis and badminton completely normally without any restrictions. Any aches and pains she might feel would most likely be due to the fact that she hadn't done much regular exercise (apart from walking) in the last six months and certainly not any really energetic or vigorous exercise. The consultant also gave a green light to all Anna's jumps and steps in dancing which she hadn't dared try, but which she needed to practise and include in her GCSE practical dance exam.

It was all good news and we left the hospital feeling delighted. On our way out we bumped into one of Anna's friends who was on the waiting list for corrective surgery. We could share our optimism and give them a positive expectation for the future, particularly as her curve was only 42 degrees (it sounded so minimal compared to Anna's 74 degree curve and she didn't have the hump that Anna had to endure). However, all negative thoughts and memories were banished by our happiness in the present and Anna could continue to keep on looking forward.

That Friday Anna began dancing again, and although her back still felt very stiff she was able to do small jumps. This was a positive achievement, albeit a small one.

The following week we attended Parents' Evening and after much discussion with all the teachers Anna decided that her 'A' level choices to A2 (second year of sixth form) would be English Literature, Drama and Psychology. Instead of taking dance to AS level (first year of sixth form) as originally planned, she would study Food Technology. This decision wasn't easy to make because, pre-surgery, dancing was Anna's favourite activity. However, the jump from GCSE level to 'A' level is a big one and realistically, after discussion with her very supportive dance teacher, Anna felt that she would not have the necessary flexibility, although she does firmly believe that in time this will come back, the more dancing and sport she does.

She made this decision without any hesitation, but with acceptance and realism about what she can do, and continually shows me how resilient she is and accepting not only of her new back, but also the different direction that her life has had to take.

She still has a residual problem following surgery in that her lung capacity seems to have been reduced and she frequently has to take a couple of much larger breaths of air during a conversation, which embarrasses her because she feels that it gives the impression that she is yawning.

We don't know whether this will ever change because structurally her body won't change position, but Theresa, our physiotherapist, recommended that we see our GP for a referral to a respiratory specialist just to check that everything is ok. She also gave Anna an exercise to do that could help to minimise this problem.

TWENTY-FIVE

Spirometer test

Now it's November and Anna has had to make her formal application to sixth form college, but after a 'taster day' at school experiencing a variety of subjects, she has decided that 'A' levels are not what she wants to do. Instead she wants to apply to a college which specialises in vocational subjects. Her choice is a two-year Level 3 Diploma to study advanced acting in the light of her changed career decision from dancing to acting.

She is full of enthusiasm and passion so it was an easy decision to submit the necessary forms and wait to see if she gets offered a place.

We also visited our GP who referred us to the practice nurse for a spirometry test to measure Anna's lung capacity.

The spirometer measures the amount (volume) and/or speed (flow) of air that can be inhaled and exhaled.

The most common measurements used are:

- Forced expiratory volume in one second (FEV1). This is the amount of air you can blow out within one second. With normal lungs and airways you can normally blow out most of the air from your lungs within one second.

- Forced vital capacity (FVC). The total amount of air that you blow out in one breath.

- FEV1 divided by FVC (FEV1/FVC). Of the total amount of air that you can blow out in one breath, this is the proportion that you can blow out in one second.

A spirometry reading usually shows one of four main patterns:

- A normal pattern
- An obstructive pattern
- A restrictive pattern
- A combined obstructive/restrictive pattern

The reading for Anna showed that she had a restrictive pattern. When we saw our doctor the following week to discuss the results, he felt that although it wasn't too significant, nonetheless it was significant enough to warrant a referral to a respiratory specialist who could then possibly refer Anna to a specialist respiratory physiotherapist who would be able to recommend specific exercises to help. He thought that the muscles attached to the ribs were contracted more than they perhaps should be due to the new position of Anna's spine and ribs following the surgery.

Anna still gets some pain in her 'hump' but says she's really only been affected twice significantly, which in seven months isn't too bad. Running and dancing are still hard for her to perform as well as she could before surgery, but she is still adapting to her 'new back' for these more energetic activities. I'm hoping that as the months continue, any stiffness will lessen considerably, because although she has switched to acting rather than musical theatre at college, she will still be covering a module on dance performance.

TWENTY-SIX

Respiratory specialist

The appointment to see the respiratory specialist arrived in January, although the date was originally set for February 6th, and Anna was looking forward to having some exercises from the specialist, or a respiratory physiotherapist (should we subsequently be referred on) to help maximise her lung capacity. I felt sure that the costoplasty had had an effect on the movement of all the surrounding muscles, leading to Anna not being able to get as much air as she needed, particularly when doing any exercise. Now that she was pretty much back to normal she was having a go at more adventurous leaps and jumps during dancing (as part of her dance GCSE work) and found that firstly, she felt very unfit compared to her pre-surgery fitness, and secondly, she needed to be able to get more air into her lungs.

Of course if Anna hadn't wanted to pursue acting as a career I don't think we would have necessarily thought about needing specific exercises and would have assumed that everything would get back to normal over time.

As part of her New Year resolutions Anna decided that, reduced lung capacity or not, she was going to do some more exercise to build up her fitness again. So, when I heard the porch door creak at 8.30 one Sunday morning in mid-January I immediately thought of Anna putting her running shoes on. A quick check confirmed this (although she had to put my running shoes on as her feet had grown a size in the nine months she had had away from any serious running!)

I listened out for her return and was impressed that it was a full twenty minutes before she arrived home. "I am so unfit," Anna gasped, but felt, like me, that it was another achievement and a sure sign that life really was back on track. She admitted that she had to alternate jogging with walking, which was only to be expected, but felt pleased that the first run had passed successfully. I asked how her back had felt when she was running and wasn't surprised to hear that it still felt very heavy and that she could feel the rods keeping her back straight. She has accepted that it could take much longer before her new back starts to feel completely normal to her, but is happy to take one step at a time.

She had good news at the beginning of February when she heard that she had been given a place on the Advanced Acting course at college. Needless to say she was delighted and it was a positive prospect to look forward to as she continued to revise and work for her GCSE exams.

The appointment with the respiratory specialist turned out to be a little disappointing because we didn't learn anything new, only that Anna's lung function was reduced. Unfortunately, due to a technical glitch, the specialist couldn't access the x-ray of her lungs so couldn't see if there was any structural problem. She was given an inhaler to see if that would help if she got very breathless. It was even suggested that she might be asthmatic, but I was quite sceptical because she wasn't asthmatic before her operation, so I could see no reason why she should suddenly become so.

The upshot was that Anna would be sent a further appointment in March with a different specialist, and before the appointment she would undergo further breathing tests.

We had another physiotherapy appointment with Theresa scheduled for March 9th and I hoped she might know of particular exercises to help, or have some specific advice regarding the breathing difficulty.

TWENTY-SEVEN

Another diagnosis

We attended the second appointment at the respiratory centre optimistic that we would find out just why Anna seemed to have difficulty getting enough air into her lungs, even during the night when she was resting.

The hospital staff were all extremely knowledgeable and very patient as they explained the purpose of all the different breathing tests, which took over three hours to complete. The different resultant graphs were explained carefully to us and to my great surprise, and Anna's, found that she is mildly asthmatic after all. After having all the relevant information explained in detail, my initial scepticism about the diagnosis was replaced with a greater physiological understanding and acceptance of the additional diagnosis Anna now had. It was just a coincidence that she had developed asthma at around the same time the scoliosis developed. Her lung capacity may also be slightly reduced because of the severity of her curve before surgery, but this should not affect her life in any significant way. In fact, it was a relief to know that there was a reason for her breathlessness and that it could be corrected by use of an inhaler whenever she needed it.

We later attended our final physiotherapy appointment with Theresa, who was very pleased with the reduced 'hump' Anna now had, and felt that her muscle strength and control had significantly improved since our last visit. She gave Anna some breathing exercises to maximise the amount of air she could inhale and then exhale efficiently, which Anna found very helpful.

Our last question related to the altered sensation Anna still had on her back. Some areas felt numb where she couldn't feel any touch on her skin, but other areas were hypersensitive and felt almost painful when gently pushed, particularly when Anna wasn't expecting it. She had noticed that when friends gave her a hug at school it was sometimes very uncomfortable because of the altered sensations.

Theresa recommended using various textures to gently rub on the affected areas to stimulate the nerve endings and hopefully retrain the brain into responding appropriately when Anna's back was touched. We collected a small bag of materials including silk, sandpaper, towelling etc with the intention of using them once a day initially while we felt so enthusiastic. After a few weeks Anna said she could already feel a difference to sensations on her back, which was an exciting development and encouraged us to continue.

The Easter holidays arrived bringing the rain and revision for the upcoming GCSE exams. Anna also decided that she would like to run in the 'race for life' 5K challenge in June (which she and I had run several times in years before her surgery) to raise money for charity, and as a bonus regain some of her fitness levels. Rachel and I also wanted to take part because the girls' Auntie Karen, my sister-in-law, sadly lost her battle with breast cancer in 2008, so we entered as a team. Once the rain subsides we can think about beginning our training!

Building up Anna's fitness and stamina should really make a difference to her feeling that she is 'back to normal' because the stamina and overall fitness is now the main aspect that Anna feels is different from a year ago. Apart from being less fit, she can now do everything she wants to and we are both looking forward to receiving an appointment next month for the one-year post-surgery consultation at the hospital, when hopefully Anna will be discharged from the system.

TWENTY-EIGHT

One year on

When I turned the calendar to reveal the month of May, it really hit home that a whole year had passed since Anna first had spinal surgery. The wait and build up to this huge event, from our very first appointment with our GP to the surgery date itself, had also taken a year, so two years of our lives had been spent dwelling on Anna's back.

Our final appointment was scheduled with our consultant who looked at Anna's last x-ray with great satisfaction. Her back had remained stable and in a good, straight position. He was delighted with the results and pleased that Anna had adapted back to her normal activities so well after both spinal surgery and a costoplasty. We shared his enthusiasm and now felt tremendous relief and joy that the scoliosis 'journey' which had begun two years earlier was finally at an end.

We mentioned the hypersensitivity that Anna still experienced in her lower back, and were reassured when the consultant explained that it could take up to two years for the nerves to completely settle down after such invasive surgery.

We left the hospital and celebrated with a special meal that evening with all the family saluting Anna's courage and tenacity throughout two years in which she also had to cope with working for and taking her GCSE exams. That in itself is a cause of stress for any young person, but Anna had taken everything in her stride and sailed through with flying colours. She still had a few exams left to sit, but knew she had done her best and was looking forward to starting her acting diploma in September and ultimately pursuing her career in films and television—a slight change from her original dream of being a West End performer, but still continuing along her path to fame!

I look at Anna now and I don't even think about the scoliosis she suffered. She can now face the future with the positive energy and drive she exudes in abundance. Her 'new' back, as she calls it, will always be a little bit different but will enable her to live life to the full.

So my advice to any parents of children facing a diagnosis of scoliosis that could require surgery, is to take each day at a time, dwell on all the positive moments, of which there will be many, and take comfort from the knowledge that one day your child will be back doing all the activities he or she loves in a far shorter time than you can imagine.

For Anna and me, the experience has had many ups and downs, but challenges faced together are not insurmountable. The surgery has been a gift, enabling Anna not only to continue to strive towards her goals, but also to find in herself the strength and resilience that will help her to achieve her dream.

Watch this space!

References and useful websites

Scoliosis Association UK (SAUK)
4 Ivebury Court, 325 Latimer Road,
London W10 6RA
Helpline: 020 8964 1166
Web: www.sauk.org.uk

www.britscoliosissoc.org.uk

www.brainandspine.org.uk/scans

www.dysraphism.com

www.orthoinfo.aaos.org/topic

www.bupa.co.uk/individuals/health

www.physorg.com/news

www.nuh.nhs.uk (Nottingham University Hospitals)

Spinal Studies and Surgery (Centre of)
www.nottinghamspine.co.uk /

www.well-women.com/scoliosis

www.curvedspine.com/thoracoplasty

www.nhs.uk/Conditions/Scoliosis/Pages/Introduction.
aspx

www.patient.co.uk Information Leaflets

http://www.bupa.co.uk/individuals/health-
information/directory/s/scoliosis

Printed by: Copytech (UK) Limited trading as Printondemand-worldwide, 9 Culley
Court, Bakewell Road, Orton Southgate, Peterborough, PE2 6XD